Eldorado in East Harlem

Victor Rodriguez

Arte Público Press
Houston
Texas
1992

This book is made possible through a grant from the National Endowment for the Arts, a federal agency.

Arte Público Press
University of Houston
Houston, Texas 77204-2090

Cover Design and Illustration by Mark Piñón
Original Art by Mark Piñón:
"Graffiti in East Harlem," Copyright © 1992

Rodriguez, Victor, 1944–
    Eldorado in East Harlem / by Victor Rodriguez.
        p.   cm.
    ISBN 1-55885-054-6
    1. East Harlem (New York, N.Y.)—History—Fiction. I. Title.
PS3568.O34885E34 1992
813'.54–dc20   92-14985
                                                     CIP

The paper used in this publication meets the requirements of the American National Standard for Permanence of Paper for Printed Library Materials Z39.48-1984. ∞

To my beloved children, Emily and Stephen, who once asked me to tell them a story.

Eldorado in East Harlem

ONE

When René Gómez was eight years old he found a silver chalice while playing in the back lot of a tenement building in East Harlem. He loved to play there because the yard reminded him of a place he had seen in a movie shot in Spain. He found an old broom stick, placed it over his right shoulder as if it were an old blunderbuss and marched around the yard like a conquistador chanting, "Al-hambra, Al-ham-bra ... " He didn't know the word's meaning, but he loved its strange sound. It was a pretty word, easy to pronounce. In the middle of the broad yard was an old stone water fountain with round columns and small lions supporting two round tiers whose pipes had long since rusted and dried. Now only rainwater and a foot of soil filled its deep basins. Tall blades of wild grass and weeds grew every spring and made it look like a giant flower pot in the middle of a concrete ground. René heard the pealed laughter of other boys as he stared at the small patch of grass in the basins and ran to them. In a long and single formation they were emerging from the back lot of a synagogue carrying holy scrolls, a large menorah, prayer shawls and boxes filled with things unfamiliar to René. One of the boys dropped a silver chalice but continued his quick march with the others, until they were all gone from the yard. René picked up the cup and took it home. His mother Amanda was furious with him, called him a thief, slapped his little face and hurled the cursed object through the open window of their front room. The cup fell on a pile of rubbish in front of their building.

That was nine years ago, he told himself as he prepared to go out for a walk. Time flies. He was older, wiser and a tough guy to boot. He flexed his arm muscles in front of a wall mirror, posed like Floyd Patterson, then walked out the door.

A merciless summer sun had beaten down the streets and people of East Harlem all day, and now the dusk, lit by a crimson sky,

7

clenched in the heat. One Hundred Third Street was pulsing with its many different faces. Children on the corner of Park Avenue screamed with joy as they cooled themselves off with the chilling waters of an open fire hydrant. A small group of men playing dice formed a semi-circle across a curb down the block. Near them three boys played congas between sips of beer. A summer crowd combed the block in pairs like tourists. And several women, dressed in long, thin, flowery summer dresses that draped the nine stone front-steps of one building, sat gossiping merrily, just yards away from the Jewish temple of Mount Pisgah. It was an old building, east of Park Avenue, that stood ominously silent and drew the attention of a gang of teenage boys who sat facing the women across the street.

"Man, that Jewish church is spooky," one of them said. "I wonder what's inside."

"Nothing, probably just benches and ashes, like a real church, but no cross," another replied.

"They say them Jews is rich."

"They say them Jews're smart."

"Maybe there's money inside."

"They killed God."

"Impossible!"

"I wouldn't go in there; it's too dark and a demon might get me!" a nervous one cried.

"Yellow!" they cried in unison.

Across the street their elders continued their blue chant until there was no one else to speak about; so they gazed at passersby and laughed or mocked them with ugly grimaces, when not arguing with one another.

"Ay, what heat!" María Cristina Cruz, a short, elderly woman, said in Spanish as she clenched a black Bible to her bosom. Her friends nodded and fanned their perspiring faces with makeshift fans of cardboard or open palms. She then turned to her friend Amanda, who lived next door to her, and asked her about her son René.

"That boy spends a lot of time daydreaming. He's also lazy and moody. Sometimes he stares at a wall for half an hour without moving. Other times he's the opposite: he'll come home with several new jokes he made up, play the radio, laugh at anything I say or make believe he's Elvis Presley. Then just as quick, the worst: he broods for hours after seeing or hearing something he thinks terrible. Then he'll say to me, 'I wonder how much punishment is enough for a guy like Hitler? Is he still burning in Hell?' 'Never enough,' I answer. Or: 'Who cares!' When he get's too vulgar or mischievous, I punish him. He knows I won't hesitate to punish him. I have a heavy club I keep next to my bed in case I need it. I don't care how grown he is."

"Maybe he's into something," María Cristina remarked.

"Something?"

"Girls."

"Drugs."

"Sex."

Amanda ignored the remarks and fanned her face with an open palm.

María Cristina saw a tall dark figure approaching from Lexington Avenue. He was bent over a dray, which he pushed slowly over pebbles, bottle caps and the earth-filled cracks of the sidewalk.

"Ay, here comes that Judío," she said.

"They say he's rich."

"They say he's smart."

"They say he's poor."

"He counts gold all night."

"Hell, he counts pennies!"

"How he scrounges."

"Why he live that way?"

"It looks like the wagon is pulling him. María Cristina, will he be saved?" a young woman sitting next to Amanda asked the old one in a mocking tone.

"No, Luz Castro. Whoever does not accept the Son remains unsaved, including women like you!"

Luz said nothing. She was used to the old woman's attacks. Besides, she'd get bored instantly whenever anyone spoke gospel.

Silas Turnvil walked slowly, almost dragging his tired legs, until he reached 113, the building where the ladies were. He was a gaunt and gray bearded old man who lived in a small room there. Turnvil rarely spoke with anyone unless it was unavoidable even when he peddled books along La Marqueta, East Harlem's main market. Silas Turnvil was the sexton of Temple Mount Pisgah.

The left side of 113 faced a large empty lot, where several buildings once stood. Here he chained his dray to the hand railing. María Cristina, who sat pressed against the black painted grid, moved slightly to her right so Silas could secure a heavy chain he used to wrap around the cart handle. He nodded in gratitude, but she turned her eyes away. Then he picked up a box of books and newspapers from the wagon and placed it on his left shoulder. He walked around to the front of the building and faced the women, who blocked the stairs and entrance. No one moved.

Silas Turnvil stared at them with a tired look on his worn face, but his deep-set eyes, blue as an early winter sky, penetrated their curious stares. They puckered their lips and crossed their legs, creating a small path, while looking in opposite directions as they formed two columns. The weight of the load arched Turnvil's back as he ascended the stairs slowly. He looked up at the dark entrance as he climbed. His jaw clenched as he winced with a slight pain. Sweat streamed down his massive forehead. His room was in the rear of 113, on the first floor. Before reaching his door, his path was crossed by René on his way out. He did not look at the old man as he whisked by. Silas closed the door behind him with a loud bang.

When he was outside, descending the long steps, René Gómez was sprinkled by a thin fire hydrant drizzle that swept its way along the street, cooling everyone in its path. He was about to step onto the street when he felt someone grab his leg. His mother told him not to disappear, then released her grip on his jeans. He replied that he had no place to go. Then he quietly walked down the block a ways, sat down on the curb, drew his knees up and rested his chin on them. The water streamed along the curb, carrying bits and pieces of small debris that seemed like small ships and rafts to René. The street lamps and the lights that came from buildings in front and in back of him shone on the water and created sparkles that dazzled him. He stared at the stream until he forgot where he was. All sounds around him vanished. But before he could adjust himself to his new state, a loud whistle snapped him out of his revery. He looked up. A member of the gang that sat on a building stoop across the street called him over, waving an arm. René got up and trotted across the street to join them.

They were a handful of boys who roamed the streets of East Harlem like a lost squad, protecting their block from enemy gangs. They had once been a part of a large gang, called the Dragons, that was now reduced in number after several members had been killed in rumbles. Others had died from overdoses of heroin. They spent their summer days loitering, robbing strangers who ventured too deep into the darker corners of the late-night barrio, and talking about the great times they once had. Most of them were in their late teens or early twenties. They spoke to younger boys like René as a generation who missed out on a great party. René, a loner at seventeen, usually shrugged his shoulders without interest, confident and brave enough to defend himself. Besides, he could never understand why anyone would want to die defending a rotten block like 103rd Street. Even rats run away when the wrecking ball tears down the old walls, he often told them. They needed each other, they said, to protect themselves from those two legged rats from other blocks, who mugged their grandmothers and stole their girlfriends. Bums with imperial names like the Viceroys, Counts, Cavaliers, Dukes, Royals—guys ready to kill for a foot of their precious turf.

"You okay, René? You looked like a zombie staring at the water," one of them said. He was called Dutch because he always wore a blue cap, like the kid on the paint can.

"Yeah, just thinkin'."

"About what?"

"Everything. I always do what's wrong. If I try to build somethin', it always falls. If I try kissin' a chick, I get slapped. I try makin' money, I wind up losing it. My mom sez dat I'm rotten. 'You're not lazy, you were born tired!' she sez. Damn!" The gang laughed. "Everyone's right and I'm always wrong. So how come da world's so fucked up? How come we live here? I hate dis block!"

"Me too, but ain't nothin' else," Dutch said.

"I dunno. Dare's also lotsa things comin' out everyday dat I'd like to get. I saw dis cat with a boss radio walkin' down Lex, lookin' cool, like he owned de world. I wanna look like dat. Da girls round here only dig guys wid lotsa bread an' good threads."

"I know a place we could find treasure," Dutch said in a low tone. They stared at him and remained silent for a long while. Dutch was a practical joker whom no one took seriously. He was also so prone to mix serious matters with sinister laughter that hardly a day passed without his having fist fights with guys he offended. The gang laughed aloud when Dutch said treasure.

"You think you Long John Silver?" René sneered.

"No, I ain't sayin' I'm a pirate, but dat temple dare," he answered pointing at Mount Pisgah, "dey say has gold inside, silver and lotsa money. You seen dem Jews come round here on Saturdays all dressed in fancy suits, watches and rings and things ... women with fancy handbags ... I say we go in one night and take what's inside. Dare's gotta be sumpthin' valuable in dare. I know it."

Another long silence followed this. For a moment each one of them imagined himself rich, basking in the splendor of wealth and comfort. Who would have thought that this wealth lay just across the street, near their homes, within arms reach, theirs for the taking. How simple and lucky! René was about to say something, anything to break the silence, when he remembered the silver chalice.

"When I was a kid I saw a buncha guys takin' a lotta rich stuff from dat place," René said. "It did look like a treasure."

As far back as René could remember, the synagogue had always been there. Once he asked some old timers about the temple, out of sheer curiosity. They raised their eyebrows, puckered their lips as if ready to blow and said that it had always been there. A solitary building in the middle of East Harlem, it stood near a garden on the eastern corner of Park Avenue, across from the great stone wall of the New York Central Railroad. The people on the block stared in silence with a ceaseless fascination at the handful of worshipers who came weekly and on high holy days. There was a time when the temple was crowded to capacity and the sounds that came from within could be heard throughout 103rd street. A cantor, a chorus and an organist gathered there on holidays and inspired the congregation to sing angelic melodies in praise of God and life. Before and after services, they gathered in front of Mount Pisgah to talk, laugh and enjoy the day. But that was long ago. As the years sped by, there were fewer and fewer worshipers who came to 103rd Street and all that remained were a few old men and women who worked or lived nearby and managed on occasion to coax a reluctant grandchild to join them. Most of the residents of the block were poor Latinos who worked in factories all day and were too tired to give much notice or thought to the curious people who passed by their decaying block. Stranger still were those black garbed ecclesiastics who entered and emerged from the Parish of Saint Cecilia all day and night in their eternal mourning. Like Mount Pisgah, the parish was on the north side of the block, flanking the empty lot, but closer to Lexington Avenue.

René and his friends continued to talk until Amanda's shrill voice called him. He got up quickly and dashed across the street, barely missing being struck by a speeding car that was attempting to bypass the fire hydrant's watery ram.

René found Amanda in the kitchenette of their furnished room, cooking. The smell of Caribbean spices filled the room as it escaped from a large pot that emitted a steady steam beneath its cover. It reminded him of an old train in a western movie. The kind that James Gardner as Maverick played cards in every Sunday night on television. The room was long and narrow with walls painted bright yellow that became even brighter on sunny days when light came in through the front window. René slept on a folding cot drawn in front of the window like a cushioned window seat. From here he could look out onto the street. This cosy spot reminded his mother of the front porch of her house in Puerto Rico. The rest of the room was adorned with rickety wooden furniture that gave the impression it had been purchased and installed there when the building was first opened. And no one knew when that had been. A small sofa pressed against a wall near René's bed. On its left side was a fake fireplace built into the wall which faced the entrance door. On its mantelpiece were animal figurines made of glass and porcelain, flower pots, ashtrays and photographs of dead and living relatives. Amanda slept on a highrise sofa between the fireplace and the kitchen entrance. She was closer to the kitchen and far enough away from the window to avoid peepers from across the street and the clamor that came in when the night was warm and the window remained opened. A large billy club and a long kitchen knife she kept near her bed were all the security she needed. Besides, René was almost a man now.

There was barely room enough in the kitchen for Amanda to move around, but she was thin and youthful enough to manage without getting burned or knocking things over. A small wooden table with a white enamel counter top, a refrigerator that had had several motor transplants and was as noisy as an old car, a small radio on its top, and a deep sink near a small window filled the kitchen. From this window she could see the backs of other buildings buried in black soil. Directly in front of this window, just inches away, was the kitchen window of María Cristina Cruz's home. From here both women spoke to each other when the weather permitted. They exchanged recipes, food, utensils, gossip or just chatted as they worked. It was very convenient for Amanda. María Cristina was a good soul in general, although she had the tendency to meddle too much in Amanda's private life and somehow always managed to interject a moral sermon into their talks. Amanda listened patiently most of the time, but there were days when she was in such a dark mood that she would tell the old woman to shut the hell up and slam the window down. Oddly enough, María Cristina would knock on her door within an hour and bring Amanda some little present, such as a flower or a cup of dessert, and thank her for being a good neighbor. I know how you feel, María Cristina would say as she came in for some more chatting.

René threw himself on the sofa when he came in from the street and sank deep into its soft cushions. Amanda yelled at him from the kitchen to sit up and reminded him that a home isn't a movie lounge. Sofas cost money, she wasn't working, he had already broken three chairs since he was born ...

"I'm tired," René said as he sat up.

"Tired? Of what? You don't do nothin' all day ... Why you hangin' 'round wit dat gang?"

She spoke to him in English with a loud, piercing voice. At times Amanda felt so riled that she lost her self-control and forgot her English. Frustrated, she'd quickly switch to Spanish. Then the words rattled out as swift and deadly as Bonny Parker's Tommy gun. When that failed, she flung the nearest object at her tormentors. And lately, René was the target, but he always ducked as fast as Kid Gavilan dodged punches.

"Dey ain't no gang."

"Den why dey jus' hang around doin' nothin' all da time. You're seventeen already, an' it's summer. You don't go to school now an' all you do is day dream and hang around. God, I'm sick of dis shit! When will you grow up? Who's going to take care of you when I'm not around? Dare ain't nobody out dare dat'll lif' a finga' for you an' me. So think!"

She paused for a moment, then gradually lowered her voice when she noticed the effect her sharp words had on him. He bowed his head and fixed his eyes on the door, staring at the brass doorknob. It reflected a distorted image of the room, with him reduced to miniature. She lowered her voice when she noticed the look of gloom on her son's youthful face. Amanda also saw in him an evolving image of someone from her past, someone that still haunted her memories.

"I bin lookin' 'round Mom, but it ain't easy. I know you think I'm lazy, but I ain't. I tried lookin' for work around Madison Avenue, but it's useless. When I do find somethin', I feel like a piece of shit. I don't want to be a delivery boy forever. Always goin' in and out of dem fancy buildings through da service entrance like a garbage man. Den gettin' insulted by flunkies in uniform who yell at me or try to hit me 'cause I forget to say 'sir,' 'madam,' or 'yes' instead of 'yeah,' like most people. Doze same flunkeys open doors, smile, say 'Hello Mr. and Mrs. Masters, you look splendid! Nice day,' even if dey look like the Mummy and his bride and the weather is shitty. Dey also treat rich gangsters as if dey are real good people, just because dey got lotsa money."

Amanda was calm now, and she listened to René patiently; letting him express his true feelings. She hoped he would take note of his own ignorance and perhaps change his ways. No one else existed for Amanda at this moment. She felt relieved when he promised to bring money soon.

"Whenever I look around and see dese buildings and summer crowds, I want to escape. Fifteen years I bin here an' never got use' to dis hard life," Amanda said when René grew silent. She got up and stood in front of the window with her back turned to him. He stayed where he was, fixing his eyes on one object in the room, then another.

"How was it in Puerto Rico?" he asked.

"Ay, I've told you a thousand times already."

"Tell me again, Mom. I like to hear about dat place."

"Dat place, as you call it, is where you an' me was born and will return to someday. When me an' your father got married he use' to take you an' me to his father's farm, deep in da woods around Morovis. Like most of da people who lived in da country, your gran'father lived off da land, long long ago. Anyway, he grew his own food an' ate or sold it for fuel, clothes, medicine an' other thin's needed to survive in dat lonely place. Most of da time, though, he gave it to his neighbors an' dey would give him things in return. People helped each other den, without wanting somethin' in return. Well, behind da *finca* was a thicket, an' behind it was a small waterfall dat cascaded into a small blue pond which ran slowly into a winding stream between red flowered trees. Ay, I can see it now ... "

"Did I go as a baby? You and me an' Pop?" René asked with eyes cast upon the dusty gray glass of the open window. Amanda's voice grew ever lower, and a sad note changed it to a mere whisper. It happened whenever she spoke about her past.

"Yeah, we use to go on weekends an' sneaked out to da waterfall. It really wasn't dat far away, but it was hard to reach wid so many trees an' bushes. Besides, most of da family were too busy working cutting cane in the fields, minding da kids or cooking. God, I'm surprised dey had time to have babies. We swam naked in da pond, beneath da cool, foamy water of da fall. You never cried nor trembled. You laughed so much an' splashed da water between your father an' me. Ay Virgen, how time flies," she added with a quick shake of her head. "Your gran'father died. Den your gran'mother followed him shortly after. I guess she loved him strongly—people don't love dat way no more—den da children scattered around da island and here. Your father died in a sanitarium, I've told you, wid tuberculosis because he never ate, drank lotsa rum and gambled over fighting cocks. Dare was other things, but it don't matter no more. Jus' remember dat he brought you into dis world an' loved you. Dat's what counts. I came here wid you in a four motor Pan Am plane when you was only two. An' here we are already in 1960, right?"

"Yeah."

"Listen, I'm going to make some money, making an' selling curtains. We're down to my last unemployment check. So go down to da basement an' bring me da sewing machine. I hope it's still dare. I don't trust da super, an' dare's too many junkies 'round here who steal from dare own mothers."

Moments later, still thinking about his mother's eternally fascinating story, René descended the dark steps of the building's basement and found himself in a large chamber that smelled of rancid water. He had entered the basement from the street entrance, beneath the front steps of 113, which he found open. He switched on a small lightbulb which hung from a chain in the middle of the ceiling. He saw a large pile of boxes stacked like a pyramid and walked towards it when he recognized the encased machine. It was so dark and quiet there that he heard no noise from the street. Suddenly, a cold chill made him want to flee from that eerie place. The stone beams which supported the building seemed like dark figures. As he pulled the portable Singer out, he noticed that a large hole in the ceiling was allowing heavy drops of water, almost in a steady stream, to fall down and soak the boxes and floor. Unable to stop it, he decided to go upstairs to the apartment above where the leak originated. René pulled the sewing machine from the tall heap of boxes, furniture and other junk. He walked to a far corner of the basement and climbed up a wooden staircase. At it's top he unlatched and opened a wooden door, which led to the building corridor. He dropped the sewing machine down on the floor with a loud thump. Then he looked up, breathing hard and found himself facing the door of Silas Turnvil's room.

TWO

Silas Turnvil, vendor, bookbinder, would-be writer, gardener, shamas of Temple Mount Pisgah, sat by his workbench mending an old volume of ancient history as he listened to a harpsichordist play Francois Couperin's "Les Barricades Mystérieuses" over the radio. The workbench was a makeshift wooden counter propped between a broad bookshelf and a narrow wall near a window which faced the building's back yard. He had built the heavy table from crates and planks gathered from the markets and lumberyards of the Barrio. It was sturdy and wide and supported all his bookbinding tools and accessories. Between two windows Turnvil had a narrow bunkbed on which he rested his old body and relished an occasional cool breeze. Just above the bed, on a bare brick wall, hung a sepia-toned portrait of a young and beautiful woman. The portrait was framed in mahogany, encased in glass and held by a thin wire strapped to a cut nail nearly buried between two red bricks. Pictured was a young woman who wore a white silk blouse that reached up to her slender neck. She was soft-skinned and unblemished, with hair curled, twisted and bundled on her head. She had dark, inquisitive eyes and small unpainted lips that sometimes seemed to move. During dark, wintry nights, in his soul Silas Turnvil often swore to himself that she smiled back at him.

For over thirty years he had crammed so many books, journals, newspapers, phonograph records and antiques into the ten by twelve foot room that he barely had any floor space in which to move around. He had piles of newspapers and walls of book assembled like a maze in which narrow paths led from one co of the room to another. Other than his workbench, books and pers, all he seemed to own was an old burgundy, velvet couch a closet full of linen and clothes.

The walls were covered from floor to ceiling with rows of

and wooden bookshelves. They contained several thousand books: some of them new, some old, some very old. At the shelf ends and between some of the books, Silas kept brass figures of Pharaohs and eagles, tin boxes, sailboats, scrimshaws of palmetto bark, ivory and driftwood carved by seafarers he'd know as a child in Nantucket. Some of the books leaned against each other in slants. Others were so tightly packed they were almost inseparable. Marcus Aurelius, Shakespeare, Poe, Irving, Hawthorne, Melville, Twain, London, Crane, Nietzsche, among others, shined in gilded splendor whenever bright light touched them. He also had many atlases, reference books, histories by Herodotus, Josephus, Gibbons and the Durants, alongside a curious set of thick books with blank pages. One broad shelf contained a Bible, a Talmud, a Koran, a Kabbalah and a Bhagavad Gita. They were written in English, Spanish, Hebrew, Arabic. Several shelves around this one contained leather bound editions of the works of Plato, Homer, Aristotle, Maimonides, Descartes, Spinoza, Thoreau and Martin Buber. Although he bound books for a living, most the library belonged to him. Some of the books he had had since his youth, reading and rebinding them with new covers before the pages withered with decay.

Silas Turnvil reached out and took a small jar of gold crystals from a shelf above the workbench. Using a teaspoon, he scooped some of its contents onto a tray, poured some pike oil over it and mixed it well until it looked like liquefied gold. Silas worked rapidly, cutting, pasting, painting titles and authors, then pressing the books between the strong grip of a large vice on the edge of the bench. After a lifetime of collecting books and cherishing them as if they were living, breathing creatures, he had acquired a gift for repairing and making them look like new. Rabbi Abe Simon of Temple Mount Pisgah called him a surgeon and a purveyor of The Word. Without men like you, Rabbi often said, knowledge would be lost. Silas stopped working and cooled off with a deep swallow of ice water.

Silas always shrugged off compliments and continued working, as if talk were a waste of time. He discouraged busybodies who asked him too many personal questions by responding with a shrug, a nod or simply by walking away. He kept an impenetrable wall between himself and others. He had no friends to visit with, no relatives to bring him joy or those endless problems that families bring. He was not new to 113, but was in fact the oldest tenant there. His next door neighbor, María Cristina Cruz, swore by her Holy Bible that he had been born in that very cramped room, perhaps created by the infernal landlord no one ever saw but whose presence was felt whenever the whiskey-pickled superintendent came to collect the rent. To María Cristina and other tenants of 113, Silas was an emissary of the landlord, set up to keep an eye on destructive tenants and blend into the ancient walls of the tenement without arousing suspicion. The truth is that Silas Turnvil had as much interest in who owned that miserable hell hole as he had in knowing who the borough president was.

Stern, reticent, vinegary and always in a rush, Silas was one of those souls who lived as if the present day were going to be his last one. At sixty-five he possessed the strength and vigor of a man half his age. Months of exposure to the sun had burned his face and set deep wrinkles at the corners of his eyes. It gave his bearded face a serene, almost sad look. And his dark, penetrating gray eyes had such a glitter and calmness about them that people often avoided looking into them. His hands were large, thick-veined, hairy, bruised, cut and swollen, but time was beginning to quicken its pace here, too, and a noticeable tremor had set in. He ignored this, of course, and painted the gilt-edged volumes with a thin brush, as if his name were Da Vinci. Tall, lanky and sturdy of body, he had a commanding voice with a sepulchral resonance that could be heard from afar. This was especially evident whenever he was on top of a ladder or scaffold, polishing a fixture or repairing a wall of the synagogue, and was addressed by someone on the far end of the place. Rabbis, students who attended schul, merchants and worshipers all addressed him from every corner of Mount Pisgah for one reason or another. Rabbi Abe Simon never had enough to say to Turnvil from the minute he entered to the minute he left. Sometimes the rabbi would come back several times and leave with an endless series of "Goodbye, Mistah Turnvil; see you in the mornink," to which Turnvil nodded until he felt a painful twitch in the nape of his neck.

The world was a smaller and increasingly dangerous and depressing place than it was when Silas Turnvil was a child. He felt the danger at his very door. That was one reason why he lived so intensely. For he tilled the soil of Mount Pisgah's garden even in winter when the ground was as hard as granite, digging deep holes to remove rocks and plant seeds for their spring blossoms, painted the outside walls of the temple every two years in a dazzling array of bright colors that often matched the flowers within the wired fence of this garden. But literature, the temple and garden, books, writing and hard work had led him into a shell so thick and invisible that he didn't even notice it. He spoke more to the plants and flowers in his garden than he did to the strange foreigners on 103rd Street. He turned the pages of a book faster than it took to say hello to a next door neighbor who may have felt just as lonely as he. Turnvil worked his muscles, pushing and pulling his wagon around, digging, shoveling, swinging a pick-ax, hoeing in the temple's garden and picking up boxes, crates, boulders the size of barrels, then walking—sometimes running miles—around Central Park for the sheer joy, until breathless, every inch of his body pulsing with life and his mind with endless plots and stories for his journal, he'd enter his room and sink into the shadows cast by his book shelves and try to create art out of the chaos around him.

Silas Turnvil was so deep in thought this sweltering August night and so busy bringing a book back to life and dreaming about the ones that he himself would create that he was startled when he heard a loud knocking on his door.

He sprang up quickly from his bench, grabbed a two foot steel pipe that hung suspended by a rope he kept nearby and, pressing his lips to the door, asked who it was. He heard a high-pitched voice, barely audible, respond, "Me!" Silas repeated his question several times and received the same nervous reply. He opened the door slightly and recognized René, although he had never spoken to him. Then he swung the door fully open until he was face-to-face with the boy.

René looked up at the tall old man but could not see his features too well. The only light in the room came from a lamp which hung by a metal chain from the ceiling, directly above the workbench. René also noticed that the old man kept his right hand hidden behind the door.

"Yes, sonny?" Silas asked in a tired, deep voice.

"I live over dare, Pop," René said, throwing his left thumb over his shoulder.

"I know."

Silas noticed that René kept his right hand inside his pants pocket. A perfect place for a knife, he thought.

"Me an' my mom, see, got things and stuff down in da basemen' dat's gettin' wet ... "

"Go away," Silas said, slowly swinging the door closed.

"Other people got stuff dare, too. It's gettin' wet by water from you," René said quickly, before he was shut out.

"Water from me?"

"Yeah. You got a leak inside."

"Go away."

"I ain't goin' back down dare. Hell with dat shit."

"Tell the super ... "

"He's too drunk."

Turnvil let go of the door and disappeared, leaving a small crack from which René could still look inside. Not knowing what the old guy was up to, he feared he had angered him enough to run for a weapon. The boys in the block were prone to mock Turnvil too often. In winter, they knocked his hat off with snowballs. In spring and summer, they pushed his wagon onto the street when he was not looking. In autumn, they filled the cart with dry leaves and refuse or ransacked it in search of girlie magazines—which he never possessed—or they simply cried out, " 'Ey, piker; what'cha doin!" Silas always replied by hurling back chunks of ice or pebbles from the open lot and spat or cursed at his tormentors, who hid between parked cars or behind the doors of the building across from 113. Turnvil's fingers grabbed the edge of his door and opened it once again. René jumped back a step with clenched fists.

"It's coming from beneath the sink, but I can't fix it by myself. Call the super."

"Too drunk."

"Yes, you did say that, sonny. I believe you. I've never seen him sober, walk a straight line or without bloodshot eyes."

"Me too, but I don't care about him. My mother's things are gettin' wet ... "

"Will you come in and give me a hand?"

René remained still. The old man's request caught him by surprise. In all the years he had lived there, Silas had never spoken to him or even given him a passing nod. Turnvil's room formed a dark corner behind the stairs and faced the basement door. At most René had on occasion caught a brief glimpse of the room as Silas quickly entered or departed; but he only saw the sides of shelves and many protruding books and papers. After a moment's hesitation, René entered and was astonished at the sight of so many books and papers, as if he'd stepped into a wizard's tower. Silas led him to the kitchenette on the left side of the entrance. It was a tiny room with many spice-filled jars, cookbooks and old dishes pressed in Rococo splendor. From a narrow window over the sink, René could see María Cristina's room, where a candlelight flickered against her dark walls. Beyond that was his home. Each floor of 113 was shaped like an inverted L that pointed to the right. Turnvil's room occupied the small loop of the L, René's the longer part and María Cristina's the left corner between them. The old man switched the ceiling lights on with a click and handed René a metal pail.

"Here, take this bucket and place it under that elbow. That's it. Now, hold this nut while I twist the one above it; it's just loose and caused the leak. Now pull. Twist. That's it. See the hole it made in the floor?"

"Yeah."

"This damn building is so old it's rotting away."

"Mom sez dat it's a miracle it hasn't tumbled down yet."

"She's right. Things like that happen all the time. Miracle or not. I think it's okay now," he said getting up, "your things are safe now."

"Thanks."

"I'm surprised that anyone keeps valuables down in the basement. There're enough thieves in this block to fill a prison."

"Dey're mostly junkies, you know."

"Worst yet."

Turnvil applied a hardening plaster to the joint they had tightened, working slow, instructing René and looking at him occasionally. He felt the boy's uneasiness and wondering, nervous eyes. When they finished, Silas cleared the area and closed the small door under the sink. René fixed his eyes once again on the stacks of books as he walked to the door.

"You really dig books, don't cha?" René said as if he were addressing one of his friends.

"No, I dig soil in a garden."

"You know what I mean. You really read all dis stuff?"

"Yes, and more."

"More?"

"I also repair them."

"Why anyone want to fix 'em when dare's so many of 'em?"

"Some people, like myself, want to keep them and read them again and again. I also fix them for other people; and sell them, too."

"You read da same book more than once?"

"Yes. I've read *Moby Dick* almost ten times. I still love it."

"Damn, I can hardly read somethin' once. What else you read?"

Silas was surprised at René's instant friendliness. A street hood like René could never be trusted. In fact, Silas was almost certain that René was one of those imps who annoyed him from behind snow mounds and parked cars. Yet, René did live just two doors away and couldn't afford to try anything foolish with a victim so close at hand.

"I read everything."

"Everything?"

"Everything. But, please, sonny, I've got things to do. Thanks for your help."

"I'm René. René Gómez."

"René, I am Silas Turnvil. Thanks again." He led him to the door. René noticed the weapon hanging next to the door, but said nothing.

"What about you, do you read anything?" Silas asked.

"Only about murder and sports in the *Daily News* and in *El Diario*, when my mother helps me with the Spanish. I love da

pictures of pretty girls: nice tits, nice ass ... In school dey made
me read *Ole Yeller*. I hated it—too stupid and sad."

"What the hell's *Ole Yeller*?"

"Boy an' dog story. Sad-ass shit."

"Ah, yes," Silas said, remembering he had seen copies of it in
a school library.

"You must be smart. I ain't never seen so many books in a
home."

"If I was smart, I'd be rich, and if I was rich, I wouldn't be
living and working in East Harlem, would I?"

Silas held a pencil in his right hand and pressed the eraser end
with his thumb until it snapped off and bounced on the floor. René
watched the tiny object roll and disappear under a large wooden
table. On its top were more jars of gold and silvery metal flakes.

"Goodbye, René. Sorry I ruined your mother's things. Tell her
I'll repair or replace whatever I may have damaged."

"What do you do with all this stuff?"

"I've already told you. I bind books and sell them. Years ago,
before you were born, I had my own shop, just across the street. I
had many books then, more than now, and people came from all
over to see me. I gave them the best bargains ... and arguments. I
often lost money because I practically gave my books away. But,
I didn't care, as long as they read them and returned and talked
for a while. Sometimes we sat for hours, discussing philosophy,
theology, theosophy, psychology, poetry, fiction, art, music, history, politics and sometimes whales and women." Turnvil's face
winced as he spoke, and a happy look changed his countenance as
if he were reliving a beautiful dream that had come to an abrupt
end.

"What's all dat stuff?" René asked, feeling overwhelmed with
the strange words the old man used.

"Never mind. Good night."

"Just tell ... "

"Well ... " Silas began to speak but stopped short when he
noticed René looking around, then sit on a pile of books. "Don't
sit there—books are made for your other end." René stood up and
asked him again about the -ologies.

"Great men and ideas. I don't suppose they've mentioned them in school to you yet, but if you stay there long enough, they will. Anyway, we spoke about everything, and I never got tired of it all. The Algonquin table was phoney compared to us, but never mind what that means. A hobo who was once a friend of Jack London told us that the greatest president we've ever had was Roosevelt. I asked him which Roosevelt, and he replied, 'Were there two of them?' We laughed a long time. We had fun then. Now they're all gone. I closed the shop after they stopped dropping by because they moved away when the neighborhood changed. And something else ... " he added with a sudden sad tone, but stopped in mid-sentence. "That was after the Second World War. Recently, they made my shop into an herb store ... "

"That's a *botánica*."

"Boe-taa-nee-kaa," Silas pronounced slowly, smiling broadly for the first time that day. "What do they sell there, anyway? I could never figure it out, they have such an odd assortment of things."

"Oh, hell, I donno. Stuff to pray with or cast spells, or make someone fall in love wid you or to separate couples one hates or embies. Dey sell candles an' powers for God an' da Virgin Mary, or to bring good luck. María Cristina, da ole lady nex' door, goes dare all da time. I wonder what she gets dare. She's weird, man. Mom buys stuff dare, too, for good luck in hittin' da numbers, you know, *la bolita*?"

"So," Silas exclaimed with a loud sigh, "people don't have time for books, but they have time and money for spirits, dreams and sham. The wooden shelves that I built long ago now support artifacts. Dumas, Dickens and Doyle have been replaced by ampules, amulets and aromatics, not to mention magic stones and plaster statuettes—things I've seen in the window display. Pagans, pagans are still here."

"I donno who dem guys are or what dem things is, man, but many people here and in P.R. believe in spirits. Me, I don't give a shit, but sometimes I'm scared of dat witching stuff."

"Don't be, René. That 'stuff' is only in their minds. On second thought, maybe Doyle would have liked it there. Anyway, I gave up trying to understand people a long time ago. One can read a thousand books and know a thousand people and still not understand them, ourselves or certain things. Life is a weird mystery I understand less each day. It should be the opposite. Hell, I don't know what to think anymore." He rubbed his temples firmly with the tips of his fingers, as if he were in great pain. "Horrors. Horrors. No one really cares anymore, not for you or for me." The old man's face grew dark and his voice bleak, as if someone had suddenly brought him tragic news.

René opened the door and walked out quickly with a sudden 'bye' and found himself out on the street again.

Silas Turnvil closed the door and bolted it, still muttering to himself. He turned again to his workbench, but stopped in front of the portrait on the wall.

"Elly," he whispered.

THREE

Later that same evening, about a mile uptown, a weather-beaten merchant marine stood in front of his dresser mirror preening himself. It was Friday night and, despite the humidity, a perfect evening for stepping out. Too many lonely nights on the high seas, away from the comforts of land, had made him feel restless. Fernando Aurelio Fuentes was the lone tenant of a one-bedroom rear-view flat on Madison Avenue. It was a three-story building with a corner bar that never closed. Its red and green neon sign blinked the words "Ponce Bar and Grill" on and off constantly, beckoning cruising women and lonely men to enter. Fuentes was a neighbor and such a regular there that the barmaids mixed his favorite drink, rum-on-the-rocks, the minute he stepped into the place. However, he was weary of spending endless nights in that cheap place, picking up women who sometimes didn't recognize him when their heads cleared after a weekend binge.

Several weeks earlier, one such woman danced with him all evening and afterwards joined him upstairs in his room, where they spent the wee hours rolling in bed. Around six o'clock she asked him to cook breakfast for her. Fuentes told her that he wouldn't boil an egg for his own mother, but he offered to buy her breakfast at a nearby cafe. On the way there a car suddenly pulled up beside them with a loud screech. A tall man jumped out, cursed them and pulled her inside the auto. When Fernando tried to free the woman, her assailant hit Fernando on the forehead with a blackjack. Fernando lay bleeding on the sidewalk until he regained consciousness. No one had bothered to poke him or ask him if he was okay. Men sleeping on city sidewalks were as common as ash cans. His head pulsed with pain, but the blood flow had stopped and clotted across his face. His money, watch and shoes were gone. He got up and cursed the day he had set foot in East Harlem. Later, he realized, it was a curse in vain because it happened again and again, until he was convinced that the only good woman who had ever lived, besides his mother, had probably died in the garden of Eden. A place, he often said, which never existed.

Fuentes brushed his hair back two hundred times until it was as sleek and glossy as a stallion's. He admired himself profusely and took painstaking care that he was as presentable as the Prince of Wales. But despite the number of brush strokes, he did not succeed in smoothing out his wavy hair; it was as futile as trying to do the same to a rising and falling sea. He had never read a story about a hero with brown curly hair. Nor had he ever seen one in a movie, with the exception of cowboys like Bob Steel, whose pictures were still shown at the Eagle Theater on Third Avenue. If he were going to succeed this time as a Don Juan, he must look the part. After all, in this racist country, he did not want to be called *grifo*, kinky haired. Blood would then flow, he vowed, and continued the long strokes.

Fuentes had a strong, thick forehead, like a boxer's, hardened by the blows he had received in his many fights afloat and ashore. His forehead was bordered by bushy eyebrows as dark as his head and mustache. Although he was a heavy drinker, his large round eyes were as clear and white as the starched shirt he was buttoning at the moment. Two small mirrors beside the large one showed him angles of his face he could not see otherwise. He wiped small shave nicks with licked fingertips and stared at his right and left profiles as if he were looking at strangers who could not see him. But when he smiled, they also smiled.

Although he worked abroad most of the year, sailing from one continent to another, the lure of New York always drew him back to its teaming shores. Small apartments and cheap furnished rooms were always easy to find in East Harlem. He would always find a flat in which to throw his stuffy duffel bag from his shoulders and always a bar or cantina nearby with plenty of "rum an' ladies." A wondering mariner since eighteen, Fuentes grew penniless and restless after several weeks of debauchery on land. Then he would run to the nearest dockyard and the open sea. Destination: anywhere away from New York.

Eventually, after spending weeks and months between sea and sky, ordered about by the officers on board as if he were a galley slave, Fernando Aurelio Fuentes became convinced that, like the greater lot of merchant sailors, he was condemned to wander the globe and find nothing but misery. In his darkest moments, in a hotel in Hong Kong, a beach in Hawaii, or in a dusty and bigoted Southern town, he thought of East Harlem, and he would once again head towards it, like red salmon heading upstream, Ishmael looking for a home ... the Big Apple, the Barrio, *la colonia hispana*, heaven, hell's favorite city: New York, New York.

"Nueva York, Nueva York," Fernando sang in Spanish as he fixed his neck tie, "how can I forget you?"

Whenever he looked at a sunlit smile on a pretty Latino face, he remembered Puerto Rico. East Harlem, with its savage jungle beat recalled the naked wildness of El Yunque, the rain forest where the Indian god Curacan still ruled. "Nueva York, I love you. Nueva York, I despise you." He downed another stinging shot of rum and looked around.

A scrimshaw depicting an ancient mariner, a small brass bell, a broadside on a wall and a large triton shell and furniture bought dirt cheap from neighborhood superintendents and the Salvation Army decorated the small apartment and added a slight cheer to his otherwise drab living room. It reminded him of a shipboard cabin. Always on the move, he needed nothing else. Fuentes hated being tied down to people or objects.

Satisfied with his appearance, Fuentes finished his drink, poured himself another one and turned on his radio. He smiled at himself in the mirror when he remembered how his shipmates often called him Meduso for reasons unclear to him. He did not mind the tag. In fact, he used the nautical cognomen on certain occasions.

A male voice, soft, low and passionate sang over the radio a sad *bolero*: "Yo quiero tus labios, tus ojos, tu cara ... linda mujer"—I love your lips, your eyes, your face ... beautiful woman. Fuentes rose with a start, brought a broom from the kitchen, pressed it tightly against his body and started dancing with it as if it were a tender woman dancing with her lover. He raised his right arm and clenched his fist as he always did while dancing with a lady. He checked his steps, smiled at her and pulled her closer. Once, she slipped from his grip and slammed to the floor, but he picked her up and started over, leading her around with skill and dexterity. When the song ended, a breathless disk jockey reminded listeners to always drink *cerveza* Schaefer, "*¡Fría!, ¡fría!,*" before dancing a fast mambo. Fuentes leaned his partner against the radio and sat the number out. Never sweat before a big dance.

He sat back, feeling very relaxed and rested before going out for the night. He reached inside his beige suit jacket and pulled out a large silver cigarette case. It had a lighter attached to its top end. With a snap, the case split in half and revealed two rows of Camel cigarettes on each side. He pulled one out, lit it and leaned back. His head ached from a recent clobbering, but the rum numbed the spot. He sat further back with his head resting on the chair's crest. Looking up, he saw a large black fly buzzing in circles above his head. He puckered his lips and tried to gas the insect with a jet of cigarette smoke, but the tiny creature escaped the cloud of smoke. Fuentes laughed aloud and turned his large dark eyes to the chipped ceiling. The dry paint hung down with sharp corners and pointed ends and reminded him of inverted sailboats, the kind that zoomed by big ships, cutting wind and waves like a knife.

He watched them from the bulwarks when he worked on deck as if he were watching a movie he wished to be in. Once, he waved at a bikini-clad beauty who stood in the bow of a speeding motor boat, gripping two cleats, while her long blond hair waved in the wind, sparkled with sea spray as if she were a living figurehead. The boat's pilot ignored her and steered in circles. When she noticed Fuentes and other men peering lustily, she removed her bikini top and freed her full, round breasts. Her loud laugh could be heard aboard the merchant ship. Angry, her companion abandoned the wheel, ran up to her and wrestled her on deck, desperately trying to cover her, while the boat spun around madly like a large toy run amuck.

There was a coffee table in the middle of his living room with a large wooden jewelry box on its middle. Fuentes got up, flipped the lid open and pulled out a handful of multicolored handkerchiefs. These were presents given to him by past lovers. Whenever he succeeded in seducing a lonely lady, he would ask her to knit a monogram on a corner of her favorite handkerchief and give it to him as a token of their love. He prized these cloths as comforters during long days at sea and in foreign lands. He sniffed their perfumes and closed his eyes. They smelled of jasmine, Spanish perfumes like Maja, Florida Water, toilet water, Orange Ice lipstick, Evening in Paris, female body scents. One venturesome woman who was fond of sporting a "bald beaver" had rolled a winter harvest of her black pubes into a ball and wrapped it in a pink handkerchief. The others contained red lips, hearts, flowers, birds, initials, names, dates and a tiny *coquí* frog embossed in gold. Whenever he sniffed a precious hanky with eyes closed he tried to guess who gave it to him. Was it Carmen? María? Luz? Linda? Rosa? Helen? Dagmar? Zocorro? The other Carmen? The other María? *¡Ah bueno!* Doesn't matter. If he guessed correctly, he relived the moments he had spent with her, in particular the way that she loved being fucked. It was a game he played often and one in which he usually guessed correctly and in which he never ran out of memories. When he did forget, he slipped into fantasies and embellished dreams, until he worked himself into an uncontrollable erotic frenzy. "I could have done this to her—I should have done that ... " he would say as he puffed deeply and bit his lower lip. Two billows of smoke blew down from his nostrils.

The jewelry box reminded Fuentes of the large trunk that lay beneath his windowsill. He went to it and turned a combination lock until it snapped open, unhooked the lock and pulled the lid up. He took out a large woman's kerchief depicting black Tulips and white Trumpet Daffodils against a red background, a gold-colored starfish frozen in clear glass and a silver woman's comb lined with a dozen mercury-head dimes. Here he also kept several chains with carved or painted pictures of religious images. A woman always trusts a guy who wears a crucifix, he told his friends. Fuentes did not know what he was going to do with these things, but he hoped they would someday bring him some emergency money. A slight precaution he always took. With his over-drinking, over-spending and wandering everywhere, buying drinks for every tramp and pickup that asked him for a handout, he could not afford to be penniless. He stared at the objects and weighed them in his palms, as if they were gold nuggets. They wouldn't bring in much, but because of their novelty, he might get enough money to stay in

New York a bit longer than planned. No, he thought, I won't sell them yet. So he buried them deep beneath a bundle of clothes and snapped the lock shut.

When he finished his drink, he ducked the cigarette in an ashtray and locked his living room window. It was a few minutes before midnight and unusually quiet for a Friday night. Although he was free to go out on the town on any night, Friday night was always special: on Social Friday nearly everyone in the Barrio found a place to go. He turned the ceiling lights off and walked out the door.

About half an hour later a dark and silent figure emerged from the shadows of the back yard, brandishing a crowbar. René stood on a spot leveled with Fuentes's second floor flat. He ran down a sandy slope, stood on an upturned garbage can until he reached the bottom rung of the fire escape ladder, and climbed it and the staircase. The crowbar, tucked under his belt swung back and forth, now and then lightly tapping the iron stairwell. When he reached the sailor's home, he pried open the living-room window, then entered with caution, gripping the tool tight and swinging it in small circles and tapping furniture like a blind man with a cane until he found the light switch near the entrance and flipped it up. René did not know Fuentes, and only decided to break in when he saw the dandy walk out the front door. Uncertain of the man's plans, René feared that he might return soon. He may have just gone out for a short while. He might still be in the building. René placed a wooden kitchen chair against the doorknob, but it was a rickety old chair that could be smashed with a good kick. He pulled down a pair of bamboo shades over the windows and moved swiftly. His heart raced so fast, he could almost hear it; the pulse reached his very ears. He hoped that the man would walk as far as hell and not return. The chances of being caught and killed were great; these things happened around here often. He had read in the *Daily News* that a burglar had been surprised a few blocks from there, was struck with a blackjack and thrown from the roof. A sign on his chest read, "He robbed the poor." The words rang in René's head as he looked around. Fuentes's place smelled of perfumes, cologne, tobacco, stale food and cheap rum. René breathed fast, feeling the fumes cutting into his heaving chest.

He entered the bedroom. A double bed with brass headboard and night table next to it filled most of the tiny room. On the table was a small lamp, a box of tissues and a telephone. He switched the lamp on, but the bulb only had 15 Watts and produced a dim glow which barely lit the room. Turning quickly towards the bed, he suddenly tripped over a shoe box and fell down. The box's contents spilled on to the floor, making a loud rattle. It seemed as if someone had opened a jack-in-the-box and a thousand clowns with bells had emerged laughing, jingling. Then it stopped. He remained laying there, nearly paralyzed. He listened to the world around him. He heard the sounds of a squeaking bed and a couple crying out in ecstasy in the room above. A sudden sensation reached his groin and excited him. He forgot where he was or what he was doing. He sat on the edge of the bed and it creaked like the one above. Then a scream cracked the air and the sounds of shouts and crashing dishes and metal pans emerged from the apartment next door. René got up and continued his search. He pulled open the night table's small drawer. Inside were several washcloths, the July issue of *Playboy* and a box of Trojans. Nothing worth taking, he thought, and continued his search. He kneeled down beside the bed until his forehead touched the floor and pulled the bedspread up to look underneath. He saw something there that made him want to scream out and run. In the shadowy and dusty darkness beneath the bed he saw the body of a dead man. A cold chill ran across his body and sweat suddenly poured from his face, as if he had received a hard slap. A deathly paleness covered his face as he tried to yell, but he covered his mouth and muffled the scream. It couldn't be, he told himself, and looked again at the spot, his heart still racing. He surprised himself and with a sudden boldness he got closer. The body was nothing more than an old pair of leather gloves dyed a very light tan, almost skin color, that laid beside a long duffel bag. He got up and walked to the living room. He noticed the small box on the coffee table and opened it, but found nothing worth taking. The trunk then called his attention.

He pried the lock open with the crowbar and sank his trembling hands deep inside until he touched its bottom. He found the floral kerchief, the starfish and the silver comb. He brushed these aside, looking for cash, jewelry, something of value, until he scratched the floor of the trunk without finding a single bill or jewelry. "Shit!" he screamed between clenched teeth and slammed the lid down. He ran around the rest of the place, opening every draw he found, tearing up chunks of carpet, spilling out a can of rice, emptying a box of Bandaids, but René found nothing. He returned to the trunk and pulled out the comb, the kerchief and the starfish. He held them in his open, trembling palms and stared at them with renewed interest. René had never seen a silver comb like it before. He spread the kerchief flat on the floor, placed the comb and star in its center and drew its four corners together. Then he stuffed the three items inside his shirt and was about to give the place a final going-over, when the sound of footsteps approaching the door and the rattling of keys stopped him cold. He ripped the shade from the window and jumped out onto the fire escape. He tore up the iron stairs, gripping its round handrails with both hands, pulling himself up with quick motions, skipping steps, dashing past open windows and up onto the black roof. As dark, silent and swift as René was, he was still spotted by several irate tenants who yelled and cursed him. He ran across several rooftops until he found a roof door open at the end of the block and entered the building. He walked down slow and quiet to avoid further suspicion, balancing himself with the wooden handrail and wall until he reached the ground floor. Once outside he walked casually, as if he had just visited a sick relative. Then he dove into the midnight crowd which streamed up and down Lexington Avenue.

Everyone ignored the fast moving, sometimes sprinting René, as he quickened his pace, heading towards 103rd Street as if he were being chased by killers. About two blocks away from his street, he turned many heads as a speeding car screeched to avoid hitting him when he ran across its path. The driver cursed at him, but René did not hear him. He thought he saw the man in the apartment following him, felt his eyes and claws reaching out to him. Footsteps grew louder and louder with every turn he took. Voices laughed at him and cursed him as he trekked his way home. Finally, just about to turn the corner of his block, he stopped when he heard someone call out his name. In his rush, he had bypassed his mother and Luz Castro, who were heading towards Lexington.

Amanda wore a low-cut green dress that draped her ankles.

Over the dress she wore a black net with a honeycomb grating which covered her shoulders, back and chest and reached down to the hem. Her hair was dark and shiny and brushed into a bun in back. Her lips were painted deep burgundy. Luz wore a sorrel dress which hugged her wide hips and underlined her knees. She too was painted, glimmering and cheerful.

"René, I'll be home late tonight. Don't stay out any longer, it's past twelve. Where you been?"

"Just walking. An' looking for a job."

"At dis time of night?"

"Yeah, well, like some groceries never close. Anyway, see you tomorrow."

"Forget it."

"Where're you goin'?" René asked his mother.

"Never mine."

"We don't know yet," Luz said.

"No, we don't know yet. Maybe to a friend's house or maybe to the Caribe Palace for some dancing."

"Well, see you. Watch out for those slick guys at da club; it's true what dey say about dem guys. Specially dem horny hicks; dey ain't as dumb as dey look."

"Shut up an' go home! I can take care of myself. Don't forget what I said, go to sleep."

They turned and walked away. Luz smiled at René, winked and blew him a silent kiss when Amanda was not looking. He stared at Luz's bouncing buttocks as she wiggled away, laughing. He ran down the block and entered 113. Once inside, he immediately sought a secret place in which to hide his catch.

FOUR

When they reached Eighty-sixth Street, Luz and Amanda turned left and headed towards Third Avenue where a night club called the Caribe Palace drew their attention with its flashing neon sign. Although the entrance was small and led to a long stairway leading down to a lower level, the sign was almost the size of a Broadway theater marquee. Surrounding the words Caribe Palace were small palm trees that blew in the wind beneath sea waves that seemed to move as the neon tubes changed from green to yellow to red, then green again. It was shortly after two when Amanda and Luz strolled along the street, stopping to look at the many window displays. Even before reaching Eighty-sixth, they had felt relieved when the men who walked by them changed their behavior. Some of the men blew kisses and lavished compliments at them. Luz and Amanda welcomed some of these *flores*, compliments, but felt irate when a staggering wino uttered *"¡Ay, Mami!"* at them. *Americanos* were different. They walked alone; in pairs at most and never drank in public; they just walked by silently and never said anything to the women they encountered. Amanda called it good, civil manners. Luz said the *Americanos* were just plain cold.

Amanda and Luz walked by immaculate German bakeries, grocery stores, bars, restaurants, and movie theaters. This rich and vibrant area made East Harlem seem like an outpost of poverty a thousand miles away.

"You think they'll let us in, unescorted?" Amanda asked Luz.

"Don't worry. They will. We're women. It's men under twenty-five they won't admit. Too many trouble-makers; these kids are getting wilder each day. The club always needs women because it's good for business. Even the very young ones under eighteen sneak in with borrowed birth certificates."

"Can't the owners tell?"

"Sure, but they don't care. Makeup, hair spray, high heels. Men love young flesh. You know, *carne fresca* ... "

"Well, they can tell if a woman is under twenty-five."

"*Negra*, the only place these guys want girls to be is under them. Including the managers. Especially the managers. What do you care?"

Luz Castro was an attractive twenty-nine year-old woman who loved night clubs and parties and any event where there was laughter, singing and lots of men and music. She had long jet-black hair, dark eyebrows and lashes, pink cheeks highlighted by a tinge of rouge and rose-colored fingernails that tipped her thin, long fingers. She dressed smartly, always prepared to step out, wearing clothes that outlined her firm, shapely body. There was no sound she loved more than a man sucking in his breath when she walked by flashing her ample naked thighs and full, round buttocks in a bathing suit or short pants. Oh how Luz dreaded New York's cold months! She hated winter for this reason solely. Only then was she forced to over-dress and stay indoors, hiding for months like a savage in a cave.

"You ever seen any real trouble here?" Amanda asked.

"Sure, a couple of brawls. But that was long ago. They have tough bouncers now. All I want is to hear music and meet a nice guy. Sometimes Tito Rodríguez plays here."

"You can keep the guys. All I ever meet in night clubs—the few I've been to—were idiots not worth a dime."

"You want to go home? You look a little down."

"No, no. I'm okay."

"Good. We'll have a fine time."

The sad look on Amanda's face quickly changed to a smile as she looked up at the club's sign. The image of the tropics, though glassy and fake with its bright, flashing colors, invoked a pleasant memory. Amanda was thirty-five, but she looked ten years younger and could easily pass for a slim woman in her late teens. She loved the attention and compliments youthfulness brought her but resented the vulgar whistles and remarks aimed at her whenever she walked down the street. Especially when it came from teen boys who were as young as René. She trimmed her eyebrows to points that outlined her light brown eyes that had just a touch of green—something her father told her ran in his family. Spanish blood, he proudly said, real Spanish blood. Yet, her complexion had a bright copper hue that never changed despite the changes of seasons in New York. Only in Puerto Rico, with its blazing sun, cool showers and sweet fruits, did she look different. On the Island, her complexion ripened to a deeper, shiny copper within hours after landing. The faded green in her irises brightened, and the whites of her eyes became as clear as flower petals.

Amanda was soft spoken, reserved, hated arguments and had the tendency to sulk whenever someone hurt her or brought her bad news. Then she would lower her eyes, pout her lips and pace back and forth in her room and stomp her sneakered feet on the thin wooden planks of the floor, while her long skirt flew round and round in circles as she looked for something to smash. She was more girl than woman, and, like a teenager out of control, she would grab the nearest cat or dog figurine from the mantelpiece, or any one of the trophies René's father had won for a victorious cockfight, and smash it against a wall. When she cooled off, she'd sulk or just sit motionless, eyes fixed on an object. Suddenly, a door knock, a car honk, or a pleasant memory would ease itself into her thoughts and snap her out of her reverie. Then she'd sing Spanish melodies that could be heard on the top floor of 113.

Luz took Amanda by the hand and led her down the dark stairs to the Caribe Palace. The loud sound of brass, strings and drums drowned out their voices as they inched their way to a table. A man in a white tuxedo jacket and shiny black pants led them to a table near the orchestra and bowed several times until he received his tip. Minutes later, he brought them drinks on the house, then lit a small table candle and placed it between the ladies. The dance floor was packed with dancers who glided around with poise and grace to a singer's tearful lament over a long lost love. *"Ay, amor, amor, amor ..."* he cried into the microphone, with lips so close to it you could hear every breath he took. Most of the women dancing buried their faces in their partners' chests and followed the singing voice and music.

The Caribe Palace was a large, dimly lighted club that drew crowds to capacity on weekends and holidays. Its walls were decorated with red wallpaper adorned with gold flowers, leaves and trees. Corinthian columns, wood carved and painted bone-white supported a second floor balcony with tables and a small bar. Patrons sitting there enjoyed a full view of the orchestra and the dancers; a staircase near the bar led to the lower level. On one end of the main floor there was a raised platform, half a foot high, where the musicians played their sets. The Caribe Palace was one of the few places where the people of East Harlem found refuge from their drudgeries and conflicts. They donned their best threads, strolled half a mile south, were greeted by ladies and gentlemen who made them feel like royalty, drank their favorite drinks, ate savory tropical food and danced all night long. From the moment an orchestra struck its first notes until the exhausted musicians packed their instruments away and the singers gave their hoarse voices a well-earned rest, the floor was seldom empty. Singers and radio disk-jockeys joined band leaders such as Tito Rodríguez, Tito Puente and Pérez Prado as they led their musicians with deft precision.

Amanda and Luz finished their drinks and ordered another round. Luz had a Cuba Libre and Amanda cold white wine. Several minutes later they were rushed by a troop of gallants who made a brilliant dash across the floor and invited them to dance a number or two. Amanda declined. Luz grabbed the first palm outstretched to her. She followed her partner amid the waves of music that vibrated from the very walls of the cabaret. She looked at the stranger's eyes and smiled. He was a slim young man in his early twenties, handsome, neatly dressed, but with a pale, hard look on his face, as if he'd been chiseled out of cold white marble. A little angel sent to rescue me. How gorgeous, Luz thought. The angel raised an eyebrow and pulled her against him so tightly that she could feel his boney chest and thighs press against her soft, fleshy body. When the number ended, he escorted her back to the table, thanked her, nodded slightly at Amanda and disappeared. Amanda sat waiting patiently, sipping her wine slowly, scanning the crowd.

"What a creep that jerk was!" Luz said as she sat down. "I gave him my best look, you know ... because I thought he was cute; and what did he do? He stared at other women!"

"You know these guys. You gotta be careful ... "

"You sound like René."

"Well, even if that baby-face had looked at you the way you wanted him to, and told you what you like to hear, and one thing led to another, it won't be good for you. You know they just want one thing. You don't need a big belly and problems. I don't look for them. I don't care."

Amanda spoke fast, high pitched, as if trying to drown out the blaring music. Her bright eyes were a bit narrow and smiling. Always a light drinker, she felt groggy halfway through her second drink. She disliked feeling high. It reminded her of her late hard-drinking husband. Memories, memories imposing once again. Her fingers traced long lines up and down her cool wine goblet.

"But you been alone a long time. Don't you miss it?" Luz asked her.

"Sure I do, but I don't think about it. Not too much. I know what I like when I see it. All I've met lately are ass-grabbers and bobbers who think I'd make a fine mistress. I don't let them go too far with me. I know my place, and I put them in theirs. I don't dance *boleros* because I didn't come here to polish belt-buckles or to harden meat!"

They laughed, drank and turned their searching eyes to the crowd, sometimes staring at the guys in the band or the singer. At times they looked at waiters who brought platters stacked with steaming meats and vegetables or drinks to tables packed with laughing people. Couples embraced. Smokers blew clouds into the air. And voices barely audible addressed each other. The world outside was shut off completely. Then there were other women. They sat in pairs, like Luz and Amanda, with lonesome, searching eyes. "There goes Carmen, María, Luz, Linda, Rosa ... the other Carmen, the other María," Luz and Amanda echoed to each other. Faces, faces in the shadows, beneath bright lights, close to the players, far from home. Some laughed, others sulked in quiet desperation. Luz and Amanda turned their eyes away.

When left alone, Amanda stared at other couples dancing by and tried to cheer herself by drinking slowly and listening to the orchestra, as if she were alone at a concert. But it was as useless as pretending to enjoy a monotonous and too familiar festival one has grown almost tired of. Yet, whenever a she saw dancers locked in an inseparable embrace, she felt an intense longing that made her envious of those dark strangers who had no right to be happier than she. Amanda thought that no one noticed the lonely anguish that was drowning her in self-pity.

Luz did not rest her eyes or tireless legs, rarely missing a number. Amanda danced several times, but always returned to her table at the end of each number and waited long periods before accepting another invitation. Her feet ached from being stepped on by drunken men with feet made of stone. Her small hands felt crushed and her hips and waist were as sore as her bruised feet. Luz twirled breathlessly to the demands of a *mambo*, slid from side to side to several *merengues*, moving her wide hips left and right in tune to the alto saxophone. She also danced several blissful, tight *boleros* with hungry men who would have devoured her very feet. Joyful and breathless, Luz reluctantly joined Amanda when the orchestra took a short break.

Luz and Amanda were about to order fresh drinks when they were approached by a well-dressed gentleman who had been sitting at the bar, staring at them for a long while.

"Hello, Fernando," Luz said to him.

"Hi, Luz. Having a good time?"

"Yeah. You know me, I love fun. Where were you? Been here long?"

"I've been here a long while, just sitting at the bar. The dance floor is too crowded. I have friends who always come here on weekends, but found none until now. Who's this nice looking lady?" He spoke with a heavy rasp that came from the depths of his throat; it was a voice adept at yelling and arguing, burnt by tobacco and strong spirits. Yet, he looked like a pleasant gentleman.

"Oh, I'm sorry. Amanda, this is my friend Fernando Fuentes. He's a merchant marine. Amanda lives in my building. First floor."

Amanda returned a cool greeting and gave Fuentes a glancing check. Although he looked like any of the other gents there and could as easily blend into the crowd from which he had emerged, something about him drew her attention. Perhaps it was the romantic mystery associated with sailors, or perhaps it was his quiet, mild manner and warm, handsome smile.

"How and where you been, Nando?" Luz asked.

"Okay. I just got back from the Maldives."

"What's that?"

"That is some islands in the Indian Ocean."

The women stared attentively. They could not imagine anyone traveling so far away. "Sometimes it takes two or three months to go and the same to return. A lot of sailors stay in port for a few weeks before returning. There ain't anything interesting there or anything special to do. India is too depressing. I was lucky to board another ship that took me to Spain and another one to Colombia and finally one that brought me back here. So," he pointed his right index finger down and around in tiny circles, "I went around the world in less than eighty days. That's faster than Cantinflas." The ladies stared wide-eyed. "Anyway, I seen lots and lots of water, strange lands and enough people to fill Manhattan. But I love New York and wanted to get back to my own people. I'm glad I'm back."

Luz and Amanda smiled at him and finished their drinks. Fuentes called a waiter over and ordered two more, "for the ladies."

"I've never met anyone who's traveled around the whole world. I always thought it was impossible. One could go crazy with all that moving around. But I would love to see South America," Amanda said.

"Great place. Big. Lots of jungles and mountains. But if you think you've seen poverty here and in Puerto Rico, it's nothing compared to that miserable continent."

"Did you see anything interesting?" Luz asked.

"I had time to visit Peru," he replied smiling as he sat down.

"What's there?" Luz asked.

"Hills, old cities, Inca Indians, crosses and churches, and people too busy working to look in the mirror and see if they're still alive. There's a lake between Peru and Bolivia called Lake Titicaca," he added matter-of-factly with a sudden change of tone in his voice and a shifty smile. "So, to the Peruvians it's Titi and to the Bolivians it's Caca." The trio laughed so loud they turned several heads in their direction. "Of course to the Bolivians it's the reverse."

When the orchestra reassembled, it struck up a hot *mambo*. Fuentes extended a hand to Amanda and asked her to dance. She took his hand and followed him to the dance floor, where they disappeared into the crowd. With deft and grace, Fuentes led her around, turning, swinging, always smiling, never missing a step or crushing her toes, like the clumsy burros who had poked her all night. Fernando smiled again, laughed, made funny faces and moved his shoulders, hips and feet in perfect time with the music. Amanda smiled and matched every step and turn with movements of her own, but Fernando was always ready, full of energy and ready to challenge her with unexpected new moves that delighted her. They followed each other round and round, their racing hearts beating with the wild Latin drums. They wound their way up and down the light wood floor like two playful creatures in a moving stream.

When the number ended, it was followed by another, then another and another without interruption. Occasionally, Luz would glide by, glued to a partner, and wink at Amanda, glad that her friend was at last enjoying herself. Then a *bolero* drew Fuentes and Amanda closer. She hesitated momentarily, then drew closer to him. Closing her eyes, she buried her face in his shoulder and inhaled the strange, tropical fragrance that he wore. It reminded her of El Yunque rain forest: fresh, floral, moist, leafy, always dark and cozy. When the song ended, they walked back to their table. Luz brushed off an insipid dancing partner and quickly followed her two friends to their table. She sat down opposite Amanda once again. Fuentes remained standing and ordered new drinks, flowers and a platter of hors d'œuvers for the women, then excused himself. He walked between small groups and couples who stood chatting in the middle of the dance floor, and vanished into the bar crowd opposite the orchestra. Here people talked loudly, shouted and harried the three bartenders who worked with rapidity and skill. Amanda was amazed at how swift and graceful these well-dressed men worked pouring, mixing, shaking, snapping, twisting things beneath the thick wooden bar as if they were playing a symphony on a giant organ.

No sooner had Luz and Amanda removed the glasses from their lips and the players struck new chords, when they were once again rushed by more men. In better spirits now, Amanda danced several fast numbers, every now and then looking in the direction of the bar. At times she was oblivious of the person she danced with and looked or smiled at her partner half heartily. She ignored their compliments and propositions. After a while, she grew tired and weary. A bit of gloom eased itself into her once again, distorting her pretty face, but she fought it and tried to enjoy herself. She was tired of the ceaseless and monotonous side show of freaks and buffoons. Her feet ached, her head pounded and, as she headed back to her table, she could still feel the presence of burly arms and rough hands squeezing her back, sides and limbs. And rude lines echoed in her head: "How lovely you are!" "I'm surprised that a dove like you has no great protector." "What eyes. What skin. What a face!" "I have money." "I have houses in Puerto Rico, bloomers on Thirty-fourth." " ... a ranch in Cancun, a penthouse on Fifth Avenue." "I have a big bed with lots of mirrors and silk sheets." "Can I take you home, my home?" "Will you marry me?" "You gotta be mine!" Ad infinitum, ad nauseam! When she finally reached her table, she found it empty. Luz was gone. So was Luz's purse. Amanda's thin hand bag was still there on her empty chair. She took it and ran to the women's room, but Luz was not there either. She hurried back to her table, hoping Luz had returned, when she spotted Luz leaving the Caribe Palace arm in arm with her last dancing partner. Amanda was about to run after her, when she was stopped by someone who grabbed her by the shoulder.

"Where are you going, Amanda?" Fuentes asked.

"After Luz. She's leaving without me!"

"I'm sure she's all right."

"But ... "

He led her to the dance floor once again. Several couples clinging to one another glided by, lost in a whirlwind of their own, face to face, heart to heart. Dawn was approaching.

"Don't worry."

"She's never done this to me. Imagine!"

"Forget it. I'm sure she's all right. Luz is a tough lady who knows how to defend herself."

A short while later, they walked up the stairs and left the club. The darkness of early morning was giving way to a warm sun that inched its way across the summer sky and dried the morning dew. It was the first time Amanda had been out this time of day, walking with a stranger whom only her friend, her vanished friend, knew.

"Fernando, please. You don't have to walk me home. I'll be all right. I live just a few blocks from here. Please. I'm okay."

"It's okay. Don't be afraid. Trust me. Luz knows me."

"I don't need an escort. It's only a few blocks ... " The word 'trust' threw her off. It made her feel momentarily nervous.

"Relax, I don't blame you for being nervous. I was once mugged by five *negritos*, but I beat up half of them and pulled out a knife. If there's anything they fear, it's a Puerto Rican with a knife."

"You beat up half of them?"

"Yes. Two of them. One ran away and the other two beat me up!"

They laughed and continued their walk up Third Avenue. But their laughter was drowned by the increasing number of cars, trucks and busses that sped up and down the avenue. It seemed as if the whole world had come alive to find Amanda wide-eyed but tired, struggling to keep her muddled thoughts in some order. Shopkeepers rattled their keys and pulled open squeaking store gates, smiled and greeted the well-dressed but tired looking couple. Gone was the rattle, roar, and squeal of the Third Avenue elevated subway. Now the sun lit the broad avenue and its many cafes, bars, antique shops, grocery stores.

"This is the first time Luz's left me flat."

"Maybe she didn't leave you flat."

"She left me alone, didn't she? Went somewhere with a guy."

"Sure. Maybe something important came up."

"Something came up, all right. I'm not like her. Not me. I go out and that's it. Too many crazy guys and killers out on the loose."

"Sure. Sure. You know what my favorite headline in *El Diario* is?" he asked smiling.

"What?"

"*HISPANO MATA HISPANA*. They print that line at least once a month." She laughed.

"There, that's better. A pretty sound from a pretty woman."

"How long do you know Luz?" Amanda asked.

"Not as long as you, maybe. I met her at the Caribe Palace about a year or two ago. Nice lady, but too lively for her own good. I like you better."

She said nothing to this, but smiled and studied his words and manner carefully.

Fuentes stopped in front of a shoe repair shop when he saw a large grey Tom cat trying to swat a moth between it and the glass of the store window. "He looks funny," Fuentes said. "Reminds me of a fast boxer."

"The moth is also fast," Amanda said as the tiny creature soared up beyond the cat's reach.

"My son may be up and looking out the window for me," she said when they got to the corner of her block.

"Son?"

"Yes, why?"

"Well, where there's a son, there's a father."

"In this case only a son."

"And the father?"

"Dead."

"Sorry."

"I loved him, but he drank too much and gambled our few dollars away. One day he got very sick and died suddenly. He coughed so much blood and water, he collapsed deep into the bare muddy soil in back of our country house and sunk into it several feet. He left me alone with René before I knew what it means to think. I hate drunks. You drink, but I don't see you falling."

Fuentes fixed his eyes on the broad grey avenue, trying desperately to understand Amanda's vivid words.

"I never fall. If I were a lush, I would not have approached you or Luz; liquor would be my friend and lover. Besides, you wouldn't be here walking with me, right?"

They were in front of 113 now. Looking up and down the street, they saw just one person at that solitary hour. Fuentes looked to his left side and saw Silas Turnvil open the thick wooden front door of the synagogue and step inside. One of the flowers Fuentes had brought had fallen at the bottom landing of 113. Fuentes picked it up, smelled it and buried the stem in Amanda's hair.

She smiled and thanked him. Amanda also thanked Fuentes for the wonderful evening. He bowed politely and asked to see her again. She nodded, then walked up the stairs swiftly and entered the building. Inside her apartment, she heard René uncomfortably tossing in bed as if he were struggling with a gang of demons in a nightmare.

FIVE

René slept badly, tossing, kicking, laying on one side, then turning to his other. The warm summer morning promised to bring another sweltering day. A warm breeze blew in through the open window and aggravated his discomfort. Large beads of sweat rolled down his smooth face, like raindrops on a soft pebble, and were absorbed into his feather-stuffed pillow. In the dream, he finds himself once again in the apartment he had broken into the night before. As he stands before the bureau, stuffing his pants pockets with dozens of coins and bills from a draw brimming with money, he senses someone standing behind him. He looks up at the bureau mirror and sees a tall man, gigantic, dark, monstrous, with an angry and sinister look on his face. It is a hideous face, unknown to him because René had not seen the man's features when he was huddled in that dark corner of the yard. René begins screaming and running. He flies out the window, but feels the ogre pulling him by an ankle as René hangs from the window ledge. He hears a loud blare from out of nowhere and everything stops. The man disappears as a sudden flood of blinding sunlight enters through René's window and lights the entire room, awakening and snapping him out of the nightmare.

Amanda had pulled the dark curtains aside and opened the broad window. René opened his eyes, sat up and looked outside. An angry truck driver cursed and yelled at someone in a double-parked car. René lay down again. He fluffed and turned his soaked pillow, then rested his aching head on it once again. He stared at the ceiling and adjusted his eyes and turned his thoughts to the real world. The cheerful brightness around him erased the nightmare.

He saw islands on the chipped ceiling, rivers, mountains and people of all shapes and sizes. It was a little game he played each morning shortly before getting up. He focused on these images and fancied himself rowing in a steady stream on a canoe or raft. He clenched a Bowie knife between his pearly teeth, like Tarzan, Sabu and Rama of the Jungle. He imagined fighting serpents, shooting villains and rescuing captured beauties who were about to be debauched by horny kidnappers, enslaved by cannibals or devoured by hungry anacondas or lions. But this morning he felt weak. There were no serpents, villains or lions. He saw himself being chased by a growling fiend, like the one in his dream, from island to island until he found a floating log on a barren seashore that took him far away to freedom, beyond the horizon.

Looking out the window once again, he saw Luz Castro descend the front steps of 113 and walk towards Park Avenue. He gazed in wonder at her glossy raven hair. It cascaded half-way down her back and hung like a curtain just inches above the most perfectly shaped ass he had ever seen on a woman. She wore a pair of white shorts that seemed transparent. He stared at her large round buttocks, hugged by a pair of pink panties. He saw them bouncing up, down, sideways, and wished that he could squeeze her gently. He silently sucked in his breath as she wiggled by and disappeared into a corner grocery store on Park. Her high heel shoes made her a few inches taller, prettier than ever. Luz seemed as if she had just bathed in a tub filled with alum; her smooth tan skin shone in the brilliance of this odd Saturday morning. He lay back and closed his eyes again, dreaming, wishing, fantasizing. He saw himself walking besides her in Central Park during one of those days in spring when daily showers wash the shrubbery and fresh grass of that great expanse. Ignoring the warm mist, they sit down on a park bench where she hugs him and whispers his name again and again. "René. René. You're so big. You're so strong. You're so brave. I love that beautiful big thing between your mighty legs." He hides with her in the middle of some dense bushes and trees, strips her. In his wild hunger, he covers every inch of her perfect body with kisses. Still in bed, he sneaked his right hand beneath the white bed sheet and touched himself. With his free hand he pressed his lips against the back of his index and middle fingers as if they were a pair of lips and kissed then. Her blissful words were ringing in his mind as he stroked himself. René nearly fell off the bed when his mother yelled at him from the kitchen to get up.

René felt a slight pinch in his lower back and remembered that he had hidden the three things he had stolen the night before in his mattress. There was a small hole on it's right side large enough for him to stick a fist through and hide the kerchief, star and the comb between two metal springs. These were useless items that he took only because there was nothing else, and he did not want to leave that building empty-handed. His booty had lain beneath him all night and had caused him the nightmare. He made up his mind to be rid of them as soon as possible. René got up and walked in short pants and bare feet outside to the corridor. A common bathroom served the tenants of that floor. It was situated on the right side of Mr. Turnvil's door, in the same dark corner. When he returned, his heart raced, and he held in his breath for what seemed a long, suffocating moment. Amanda was changing his bed sheets as she did every three or so days. She did not pay attention to the rip in the mattress and covered it quickly in her usual Saturday rush.

"René, I want you to come wid me to La Marqueta."

"I can't ... "

"Get dressed. I'll need help wid da bags."

Later, they walked along Park Avenue and entered the market beneath the rusty base of the train tracks. La Marqueta began on 111th Street amid boxes of fruits and vegetables and ended on 116th Street, where there was a large fish and meat market. Each section of the market ran from one end of a city block to another. On both sides of the avenue, merchants stacked crateloads of groceries, clothes, toys and religious items on pushcarts, vans, horse-drawn wagons and drays—side to side, end to end and between parked cars and trucks. At the street level of the tenements which faced the elevated train tracks were an unbroken line of stores. In their windows, the stores displayed canned foods, cheeses, hardware, clothes, medicines and live poultry. The shopkeepers never fought the street vendors nor bribed policemen to chase them away. As a small boy, René saw old men and women trembling under snow and frost in flat-topped hats, checkered coats and woolen mittens, stuffing bags for customers, weighing things or convincing them the clothes in their store would make them look beautiful. That was when La Marqueta went as far down as 103rd Street. Since then, the wrecking ball had demolished half of East Harlem, and tall, red or yellow brick housing projects had replaced most of the old five-story tenement buildings.

One cold February afternoon when René was off from school and Amanda was laid off from her job in a doll factory, she and René subsisted only on eggs and rice, a hearty meal for just a few quarters. He once stole a chicken from a poultry yard at the market's end, ran swiftly and disappeared into it's large shopping crowd. The shocked fowl squawked and flapped its wings madly as it hung upside down at René's side. René exited through one end and found himself running knee-deep in snow along Park Avenue. He headed down towards his block as a policeman blew his whistle and set off after him. René ran fast, but it was like running underwater, a slow and endless struggle with his pursuer just yards away. But he managed to outdistanced the angry officer.

When Amanda asked him where he had gotten the chicken, he told her that he had found it wandering alone between parked cars, lost, lonely and homeless: a market run-a-way fleeing from a butcher's cold cleaver. The bird was an old rooster who had the habit of picking up only its left wing to stretch, its right wing probably paralyzed by the cold. René named it Lefty. A week later when he came home from school, he found Lefty in the kitchen, frying in a large pan. Inside the trash can he found the dead cock's head with a pale look of horror. That night René went to bed hungry and the next morning he even foresake his daily egg because it reminded him too much of his late Lefty. He swore never to steal anything living again.

René and Amanda walked slowly through the market, picking things from the tiered stalls, paying for them and going on to the next block of stalls, exiting one end and entering another section. Outside were street peddlers who pulled things from their bags and pockets, old women who sat on empty milk crates and sold brown paper shopping bags, policemen who walked the beat on the look-out for beggars and pickpockets, thieves and drug pushers. Men and boys shaved and sold cold snowcones with colorful syrups, scooped sweet coconut ice cream from long metal bins buried in ice and covered by brown gunny sacks. And on almost every block stood a Bible-punching evangelical preacher, born, unborn and born again and again, pandering hell and damnation at the top of his lungs for hours on end without tiring or losing his voice. But this summer even these preachers' yells were drowned out whenever a campaign car or truck rode by with blaring bullhorns urging everyone to vote for Nixon or Kennedy.

The market interior was partitioned in the middle by wooden stalls stationed back to back, facing other stalls propped against the metal supports of the elevated rail tracks. Each stall had a narrow staircase on its side which led to a foot-wide platform where its merchant could dispense items or change to an assistant who ran up and down the steps, weighed goods on hanging scales, dispensed change and joined the chorus of market barkers who sang all day: "Here! here! The best! The cheapest! *¡Aquí, señora! ¡Aquí! ¡Bueno, bonito y barato!*" The Saturday crowd rushed back and forth talking, bargaining and arguing with merchants. Crying infants and children added to the confusion of the teaming market place. There were also small grocery stores and *botánicas* throughout the market, stacked from floor to ceiling with can goods, cold cuts, cheeses, spices, plants, incense, herbs. Above all this, directly over their heads, the mighty roar and clanking, and rumbling of passing trains sounded throughout the metal enclosure every twenty or thirty minutes. The crowd, the heat and the train made La Marqueta seem like the inside of a volcano ready to erupt. The rich smells of cooked food, fruits, vegetables, dried codfish, incense and herbs from the *botánicas* and flower stands were everywhere. Amanda breathed in deeply. She loved the smell of jasmine, coconut, fresh flowers and plants and strong expresso coffee that permeated this emporium.

They were walking loaded down with packages when Amanda reached into her handbag and found it open and her wallet missing.

"René, a pickpocket took our money!"

He looked around quickly and saw a strange boy, about his own age, rushing through the crowd. There was nothing unusual about this, but as he neared the exit he snatched an old woman's handbag. She held its long strap tight, like someone struggling with a wild dog, and he let go and sped outside. René dropped the shopping bags on the concrete floor and ran after him, pushing, shoving, knocking people and their packages down. Apples, oranges and coconuts rolled all around the puzzled shoppers. Grocery loads were crushed. Curses filled the air. Several dogs barked and joined the chase, but no one stopped the thief. René was a swift runner with long, thin legs that never tired. They seemed fired with an energy fueled by an anger that someone would do this to him and his mother. The thief ran east along 110th Street. Seeing himself about to be captured and beaten by the fury behind him, he dropped the wallet, turned right and headed north along Madison Avenue. René stopped, picked up the purse and trotted back to the market where Amanda waited for him on the corner of 116th Street.

"I got it back, Mom. But da motherfucker got away," he said breathing easier now.

"It don't matter. Gimme it. Thank God we bought everything we need for dis week. He almost got away wid my last five dollars."

"The bastard!"

"Stop cursing. If dare's one thing I hate is a crook." Her words had a stinging affect that silenced him. He too was a crook worthy of being tracked down and chastised. He noticed that lately she was restless and impatient. She often paced back and forth between the kitchen and the front window of their furnished room. She stared out to the street, biting her finger nails, crossing her arms, running her hands up and down the back of her arms as if they were on fire. She breathed deeply, heaving her small chest with long, deep sighs. Suddenly, she would turn around and lash out at René if he dragged his feet too much, or bounced a Ping-pong ball once too often against the walls or floor, or flipped the covers of a Batman comic too loudly.

Whenever she was sore at him, she would address him as *usted*, instead of *tú*. Lately this had been happening frequently. Yet, she was also reluctant to be too strict with him because he was growing rapidly and no longer a spankable child she could restrain by merely flashing a leather belt. She had often done this when he was a boy and had gone so far as to name the belt Catalina. René shivered whenever she mentioned that name. Sometimes Catalina would leave red stripes across his back that took days to heal. But this occurred rarely, only when René committed a serious offense, such as him going out without locking the door. Afterwards, when she gained control of herself, she'd feel pity and guilt and treated the boy with extra kindness. Now he was too old for such simple punishment. He was taller than her, seventeen, growing into a man with a strange silence in him impossible for her to understand. Anyway, she was growing weary of child-rearing and looking forward to the day when René Gómez, the grown gentleman, would live his own life and allow her peace and freedom.

Despite these spats which were brought on by a lack of understanding on both sides, there was genuine love, perhaps born of their isolation. They had few relatives and only a small handful of friends and acquaintances. Amanda would do almost anything for her only child. And René dreaded the thought of deliberately hurting or disappointing her in any way. His bad deeds were accidental, he thought. There was no way to convince his short-tempered mother that he made mistakes. Lately, in a way that surprised him, he was growing aware of her lifelong struggles and pains. He saw himself as the only one who really cared for her, the only one able to aid her in her lonesome battle to survive in a land where she never felt welcomed or comfortable.

Amanda had slept only two or three hours that morning and was constantly yawning and trying to stay awake. Strong coffee, aspirin and a long cold shower had awakened her enough to slowly move around and complete her household chores and shop, but that tired feeling that comes from over activity made her want to lay down and rest her sleepy head. When they arrived home, they placed the packages on the table. As she was putting away the groceries, Amanda asked René to check the mailbox. No response. He had slipped quietly out the door and disappeared around the corner.

On the Park Avenue side of Silas Turnvil's garden there was a fence door made from the same wire mesh as the rest of the fence which allowed entrance to the garden from the street. A narrow door on the left side of the synagogue led out to the garden. It was an old wooden door carved of oak and reinforced with black iron bars across its middle. It was almost hidden by a thick curtain of vines that covered the entire left side of Mount Pisgah from the bare soil to its tin roof molding. The green vines were inching their way up and across the back and sides of the old building, but Turnvil stopped the growth in front by constant trimming. There were also vines along the fence covered by trees, bushes and tall plants. An ailanthus tree, almost as tall as the temple, stood at the corner tip of the garden with long thick branches draped with rich green leaves. It hovered over the corner of Park and 103rd Street. Here and there a bare spot along the fence offered outsiders a narrow view of the garden and its many colorful plants, flowers and a tiny stream Silas had dug and circulated with a rubber hose and motor. Although the warmth of summer had dried many of the plants and killed most of the flowers, there was enough shade beneath the trees and bushes to allow roses, sunflowers and chrysanthemums to grow. Silas was as diligent in the care of his garden, particularly its flowers, as he was with his library. He knew that an abandoned garden dies quickly; so he watered it daily, trimmed the hedges and brambles that might block off light and removed pebbles and refuse some uncaring people hurled over the fence as they walked by. He enriched the soil with fresh earth that he scooped from Central Park and added minerals to it. The lot had been acquired by the temple when the old building which had stood there many years back had collapsed from old age. Homeless vagabonds had taken to sleeping against the temple's walls in warm weather and often created disturbances that annoyed Mount Pisgah's weekly worshipers. A wire fence was put up along the inner edge of the sidewalk where the old building had stood to bridge the gap between Mount Pisgah and a one story marble workshop called New York Marble Works in the middle of Park Avenue. The enclosure was perfect for a garden.

As the afternoon wore on and evening approached, Silas began to feel tired. He had been working since dawn at the temple and the garden. He loved the peaceful feeling of dawn and the burst of energy it brought him each day, when he hurried before a darkening sky made it too dark to work outdoors. Except for an occasional train that rode by overhead, it was unusually quiet for a Saturday afternoon. Then, gradually, the sounds multiplied and gathered momentum as evening approached and the night claimed a life of its own. Speeding trains, buzz-saw noises from the marble shop and people talking, singing and yelling tempted Silas to want to yell at the world, "Shut up!" But he restrained himself, fearing that he might disturb the Sabbath worshipers inside the synagogue. There were two white marble slabs in a corner of the garden which the owners of the New York Marble Works had given him. The slabs were about a foot wide, two feet long, an inch thick, white as mountain snow. Silas did not know what he'd do with them. Perhaps he'd replace a loose panel near the altar, build a coffee table for the recreation room or attempt carving the Ten Commandments on them in Hebrew. He loved challenges. He bent his stooped shoulders and was about to pick them up and carry them inside when he heard a familiar voice address him from the interior of Mount Pisgah.

"Don't, Mr. Turnvil, you'll break your back."

Silas recognized Rabbi Abe Simon's voice and turned around.

"Hello, Rabbi. Thanks, I can manage."

"I'll help. I'm not as weak as I may look to you." Rabbi Abe said and winked at him. Together they stacked the slabs on top of each other like inseparable books, carried them inside, placed them on the floor near the door and returned to the garden.

"What do you plan to do with these things, anyway?" the rabbi asked as he took a long, deep breath. The humid summer night and his tight suit made his face glimmer with perspiration.

"Don't know yet. I may want to replace part of that cracked wall near the Ark."

They walked around the garden as they talked. Like Silas Turnvil, Rabbi Abe Simon was a man in his middle sixties. He had a short, sturdy frame with broad shoulders and an impressive head that seemed carved of stone. At times he reminded Silas of a marble figure that had been unearthed in an Israeli dig. Simon sported a brown beard streaked with grey strands that hid half his neck tie. Always neatly dressed in a pressed suit, he had the tendency of brushing dust off his sleeves with the back of his hands as he spoke. The shamas knew the rabbi was thinking deeply whenever he did this. Silas found it less irritable than hearing someone say, "Ahh, ahh, I think ... Ah ... " Simon's light blue eyes had a sadness in them that at times made Silas wonder if Simon was about to weep or laugh; they were eyes that could distinguish a wise man from a fool with the slightest glance.

"It's an old building with several cracked walls. You take good care of it, Silas. Sometimes I wonder what keeps you going. You work hard, shun money and never complain about pain or anything."

"I do complain ... to myself. Sometimes I, too, wonder what I'm doing here."

"Here?"

"Yes, here."

"In this garden? Block? World?"

"Yes. All of them. I'm getting tired, Rabbi."

"You've been alone too long, my friend. You think too much. That comes from being a man of books. Too many books and not enough flesh."

"I don't care about that. Besides, there is no such thing as too many books. Come on, Rabbi, this from you?"

"Of course there's no such thing as too many books. Don't I read all day? You read my books, I read yours ... And I don't mean that kind of flesh. I mean like what we're doing now, you and me, talking, enjoying the evening, exchanging ideas—a little something called human interaction. You don't get enough of it, Mister Turnvil. When did your wife die?"

"Long ago, perhaps last year, maybe yesterday, a minute ago, I've lost track of time. Is there such a thing as time?"

"Time is what you make of it. One minute life is all glory, the next minute nothing but infamy all around us. No one says living is easy. Sorry I ask, there's been no other special woman for you?"

"No."

"Too bad. It shouldn't be. The world is full of good people."

"And bad."

"And bad, yes. But mostly good people. We must go on believing in good. I once read a story about a group of Spanish soldiers, I think, out west somewheres ... I don't remember, but it doesn't matter, really. Anyway, they search for some place called the Seven Cities of Gold, also known as Eldorado. In their blindness they sought a wealth that did not exist. They were the victims of an illusion inspired by clever Indians who wanted to be rid of them."

"Am I as blind? I seek riches? Coronado was a greedy bastard, like most of his contemporaries, who only wanted to fill their stomachs, screw Aztec maidens and send men to their death in order to protect stolen treasure, satisfy a king and queen's vanity, render homage and power to parasitic preachers who offered nothing but illusions to the blind and unenlightened. I don't care ... " his voice trailed to a whisper when he looked up and noticed a tired look on the rabbi's face. "Most men choose to destroy beauty. They embrace the wildest conceits and self deception. Pray hard until you sweat blood, but you can never move a mountain. No one has ever walked on water except a flying duck. I just want to be alone. Thoreau wasn't crazy; Huck Finn was Quixote as a boy; Captain Nemo sails along the East River each morning. I see them every day. Think I'm nuts, Rabbi?"

Turnvil's voice grew deep and tired. As he spoke he pressed his lips together and the muscles in his jaws tightened. He also kicked small mounds of dirt with his shoe tips at the end of each sentence. They walked around the garden in small circles while the crackling sounds of the buzz saw from the marble shop echoed against the granite wall of the railroad and added to the din of passing trains.

"No, I don't think you're nuts. I move mountains every day and can live inside a 'great fish' if I want to, but only in here, where it counts." He pressed his right hand over his heart.

"Shall I leave?" the rabbi asked.

"No, please."

"I didn't mean to compare you to Coronado. I only meant to say that men like you can spend a lifetime looking for something that isn't there. What that is, only you know. All the wealth of this world is within you—you know that as well as I do. My friend, you are an enigma, a goy with the heart of a yid, a wandering Jew seeking a soft meadow in which to rest his aching head without fear and spread love and knowledge to a dark world. I've never met anyone like you. But, tell me something, Silas. Would it be too much if I were to ask you about your wife? What was she like?"

A long silence followed as Silas thought about this unexpected question. No one had asked him that in many years. But the rabbi was someone special. Not in the habit of prying into people's affairs, Simon hesitated at first, then went ahead, knowing that Silas Turnvil, firebreather that he was, had a sensitive side and would say something, anything, to keep the conversation going. Silas liked the rabbi that much.

"There really isn't much to say. We met many years ago near a large green lake in the country, somewhere out West. I drifted six years or so before coming to New York. We courted for several months, married and came here shortly before the Depression. We had no relatives, friends or good neighbors here, just each other. You know how indifferent city people can be. I remember the happiness I felt coming home every evening after working all day for peanuts in a Bronx lumber yard. I would find her singing softly while playing an upright piano I had traded for a Model-T Ford; or she might be reading, watering plants, setting our dinner table ... She could always tell when something was troubling me. Strange how women can do that. Well, if I remained silent, she pried it out of me, ran her soft fingers across my face and just smiled—that's all! I didn't need anyone or anything else. When I opened my bookshop, she spent more time in it than I did. The neighborhood changed after World War Two. We sold fewer books as time passed, so I continued to work wherever I could find someone willing to hire an all-round man. I sold newspapers, books, wrote short features for the small press and book reviews for dailies, shoveled snow and coal—anything to keep my cozy home and Elly. Even my love of books I acquired from her. Well, I left her alone in the shop one dark winter night and went for groceries just two blocks away. Then a gunman held her up, gagged her and tied her to a hot radiator ... then he shot her in the chest. Elly never had a chance to flee. The maggot got away with a miserable thirty dollars. Nowadays people get killed for less. Even a silly argument over the shape of a man's mustache can cost a person his life. No amount of punishment is enough for a heartless fiend."

" 'The evil that men do lives after them ... ' "

"Thank you, Master Will. Sometimes I think you read too much, my friend."

"Look who's talking."

They walked out onto Park Avenue. Silas placed a heavy padlock on the wire-mesh door.

"Why do you bother with that lock? It's like closing a house without a roof. All one has to do is climb the fence and jump in," Simon said.

"I always hope they'll rip their pants off and scar their bony asses in the process." Their loud laughter echoed against the granite wall of the railroad.

Evening was approaching, and a twilight glow that lit the sky induced the two old men to continue their chat as they strolled west. About to walk through a tunnel walkway, they were bypassed by René, who emerged from the opposite end in a mad rush until he reached the east side of the railroad track.

SIX

One warm early afternoon René sat leaning against Silas Turnvil's garden fence cooling himself off in the shade of some greenery. His face and arms stung from sun exposure. After spending several hours roaming around the barrio looking for work or diversion, he returned to his block empty-handed and crestfallen. He'd gone to La Marqueta and asked a fruit vendor for a job. The merchant shook her head. René then picked up three lemons from her stall, guessed their weight, flipped them in the air and caught them in mid flight with a brown paper bag he snatched from her hands. Good catch. Good guess. No deal. A druggist on Madison Avenue told him to get working papers and apply in Christmas. And at a corner candy store, the owner told René that he didn't need anyone at the moment, but in the spring of next year he would need an experienced soda jerk.

René, feeling dejected and mocked, returned to 103rd Street to rest and figure out his next move. Off his feet at last, he felt relaxed, somewhat sleepy. A soft breeze rustled the branches of the ailanthus tree he sat under, which made the leaves hum in the wind. He was nearly nodding. The sharp sound of a bush trimmer behind him made René turn his head around. He saw no one at first, but the clipping intensified and soon he was able to see Silas Turnvil's bearded face inside the garden. Tiny twigs and thick leaves surrounded his face and chest.

"Hey, sonny, if you don't want a haircut step aside. These clippers are long and sharp," Turnvil warned.

"I ain't no 'sunny,' Pop. It's me, René."

"Ah, yes. My brave neighbor. And I 'ain't' your or anyone else's Pop. Ow!" he suddenly yelled when the large scissors slipped from his hands and landed on his toes.

"You okay, Mr. Turnvil?"

"Yes ... "

Before Silas could finish his sentence, René got up and quickly ran around the fence and joined him in the garden. Although René had seen Mount Pisgah's garden from the temple's roof and from the rooftops of the buildings across the street, this was the first time he'd set foot in the pretty enclosure. Several times he had wondered what the old man did as he moved around the bushes, flower beds and tiny water stream. René was also curious about Silas's constant movement in and out of the dark, usually empty, temple. René scanned the garden and Silas as the old man picked up the scissors and placed it next to a shovel, a rake and a hoe that lay on the ground.

"Can I help you with anything?" René asked Silas.

"Not really. What do you know about planting and growing things?"

"Not much, I guess."

"Well, okay. Here."

Silas handed René a rake. Using his hands and arms, he waved an invisible rake back and forth. René did as instructed and before long they were working the garden, raking, digging, cutting and planting seeds or sprinkling the green foliage with a garden hose. René enjoyed aiming the nozzle at the tree stems and bushes along the fence. It felt good to be watering this bare soil. It was different from the times he'd played with the corner hydrant, where water slipped along the black asphalt and vanished down the sewer.

Loosing all sense of time, René stayed with Silas several hours, working, questioning him and listening to the old man's words as he spoke about the garden, old Harlem, books. Unaware of himself, Silas entertained and taught René things he once believed he'd never share with anyone in the barrio. Perhaps Rabbi Abe Simon's words had touched a chord in him which helped Silas relax and treat René as if he really mattered.

It was not until the loud sound of the noon time siren rang out that Silas led René to the fence door. He thanked and invited René to come back some other time. With inflamed hands, René went back to where he'd been earlier and rinsed his hands beneath the mild flow of the fire hydrant. It was growing dark now, and he turned towards his building, suddenly remembering what he had hidden.

When René arrived home, he found his mother dozing on her narrow cot beneath the warm glow of a dim lamp which hung on the wall a foot away from her head. A romance novel lay half opened across her heaving chest like a large A. He tiptoed over to his bed and knelt between its left side and the window. Digging his hands between the sheets, he pulled the star, the comb and the floral kerchief out from the hole and stuffed them into his shirt, but left one button open in his rush. Quietly, so as not to wake Amanda, he smoothed out the bed and sat on its edge, where he remained for a few moments staring out the window. He felt almost as nervous as he had the night before, when he had committed an act which confused him. Dreamer that René Gómez was, he never thought that stealing would bring an end to his and his mother's money problems. Poverty was a normal way of life. Yet he figured that if he could gather enough money, perhaps they could move out of the barrio, maybe to Puerto Rico, a place he'd never seen except through infant eyes. She would at least stop pestering him with her daily "Find a job! Find a job! Do-somethin'-to-help-me ... " singsong. Now what started out as mischief brought on by boredom and weariness had, to his surprise, awakened in him feelings of guilt, confusion, nightmares. He decided to be rid of the loot immediately. But where? And sell it to whom? How much could he get? He had seen similar junk gathering dust for years in second-hand stores along Third Avenue. It did not matter.

He got up and walked across the room towards the door. Although there was loud music coming from the room above, as Luz Castro waltzed around her place singing and dancing, Amanda did not budge. But when René reached out to pull the doorknob, the comb slipped out from his shirt and made a sharp sound as it landed on the floor. It awakened her.

"Is dat you, René?" she asked in a tired voice.

"Yeah, Mom. It's okay, go back to sleep."

"No, it's too early. I didn't mean to fall asleep." She got up and flipped the light switch near the door. Then she noticed the comb on the floor and asked him what it was.

"I think it's a comb. Take it. It's for you," he said quickly as he picked it up and handed it to her.

"Why you givin' me dis? Anyway, where you got it from?"
"I found it in a back yard. Take it. I didn't have time to
remove the dimes. All of dem have mercury heads, may be worth
somethin' in La Marqueta. Give it to a coin collector. Bye, see
you later." He opened the door and walked out fast.

"Don't stay out too long," Amanda said as she took the comb
and locked the door. "Too many bad things happen on Saturday
nights."

After many years of agonizing over the words in the Bible, and
seeing the world sinking deeper each day into what she considered
moral decay, María Cristina Cruz was convinced that the world
was about to end soon. How soon she could not say, but it was
inevitable.

Deep in thought, she walked slowly along the shadows of Park
Avenue. Since early morning she had been struggling to rid herself
of the feeling that something terrible was about to happen. Perhaps
it was just fatigue. Her old body, though sturdy and able to move
about at a quick gait, suddenly developed aches and pains where
she had never felt them before: her head, neck, lower back seemed
to pulse with a prickling sensation, and her dark brown eyes felt
a burning which grew worse as the day wore on. Mistrustful of
doctors because too many of her acquaintances had lately entered
hospitals and were never seen again, she decided to just lay down,
hoping that perhaps a little rest would calm her unsteady nerves.
But the rest turned into a deep slumber which produced bizarre
dreams. She got up with a snap when someone threw a large glass
bottle from the roof into the back yard. "Pigs," she grumbled, rose
and went out for a walk along the East River. An hour or so later
she returned home as the street lights went on one by one.

María Cristina had lived alone in that furnished room for over
thirty years. A short, stock woman nearly sixty, she spent her
days walking the streets of East Harlem handing out leaflets and
flyers given to her by the pastor of the Church of the True Truth,
an evangelical store-front establishment with branches throughout

the city. Dour, stern and prone to always bring the Gospel into conversation, she rarely opened her door to anyone. It was a way of assuring herself that her home was free of danger, a sanctuary in the midst of a jungle. Amanda dropped by occasionally, but their talks were brief because Amanda was always in a rush and always made excuses for not accompanying her to church. Yet, María Cristina had once confessed to Amanda that she had been married. She was born and raised in the deep woods of central Santo Domingo, where she had spent her youth and early womanhood roaming through the open fields and running errands to the *pueblo* for her parents. When she turned thirty she met a man from the capital who was looking for a chaste woman to become a good old-fashioned wife, "a rarity" these days, he said. They were married, but a month later he ran away with the wealthy widow of an undertaker. He wrote her a letter soon afterwards telling her of his decision and went so far as to confess his passion for the widow, " ... a woman full of life, living in my soul, with breasts like a Greek goddess." Eight months later María Cristina gave birth to Jorge.

Bitter, hurt and confused, she took the letter to a spiritualist. María Cristina told him the sad story. Yes, he said, her husband had been hexed. The letter and a strange scented handkerchief he'd left behind proved it. They contained enough evil incense to separate the tightest bonds of the human heart. He closed his eyes and told her about other wonders. She joined his spiritualist order as a firm believer until its leader, this very prophet, put his hands between her legs when he thought she was in a deep trance. Then she did the running away.

In New York, she felt more alone than in her country but adapted to her new world rapidly. From the onset she stayed indoors as much as possible. Alone, friendless and betrayed by several men while still young-looking, she found refuge, peace and work in church. There she made new friends, sang hymns and helped feed, clothe and shelter the needy. Now in her old age, María Cristina became so zealous and immersed in the sacred text that she abandoned her needs and sometimes went for days without eating. Her loose skin hung from the edges of her thin body like limp cloth. At times Amanda thought that María Cristina had finally cracked and would either be taken away in a straight jacket to El Bellevue or be discovered as a mummified body in her room.

María Cristina's room, like the others in 113, was long and narrow and had a tiny kitchenette to the left of the entrance. Its bare wooden floor creaked in places where water spills had eaten away its dark brown paint. A small single bed, a coffee table, a flower stand made of mahogany which supported a large black radio, a dresser and her altar were all her furnishings. The altar was a long and narrow pine box draped with a white sheet which was adorned with numerous holy pictures, statuettes and glass-encased candles of various colors. Above this altar, high up on the wall, were two wintry black and white photos. One was of María Cristina taken sometime during her late forties. Though she wore a half-sad expression, the picture also captured a noticeable youthful look on her face. The other was a curious picture which she never tired of looking at. This was a trick photo of a handsome man in his early thirties who sported a thin mustache and wore a black beret tilted down the left side of his head. He sat at a round table playing cards with three other men who were his exact same self, as if he were facing a group of mirrors. The man in the picture was María Cristina's only child, Jorge, who had died recently of sclerosis of the liver. He had been an incurable alcoholic.

She turned her radio on, walked to her window and opened it, then sat down on a kitchen chair which stood between the window and the altar. The radio dial was set to a station devoted solely to preaching.

"Blessed is the one who reads the words of the prophesy, and blessed are those who hear it and take to heart what is written in it, because the time is near," a soft-spoken man said in Spanish over the air waves, as he read from the Book of Revelations.

María Cristina rubbed a warm balm along her arms and neck. She winced as its pungent fumes further stung her eyes.

"Look, He is coming with the clouds, and every eye will see Him ... "

She drew the curtains aside and pinned them to their bows on the wooden window frame. Then she leaned back and looked outside. Except for a trickle of light that came from 113 and the opposite house, the yard was black as a coal mine. She saw nothing but the bare brick wall of the building and heard several voices laughing, singing and arguing. She remained seated, breathing in a warm breeze. As the preacher spoke and his voice grew louder, María Cristina suddenly remembered the rumor that had spread throughout the barrio the year before and was convinced that it was the cause of her pains and torment.

In 1959, word had spread rapidly throughout East Harlem that 1960 was going to be the year of Armageddon. None of her church friends could imagine Earth living another year "in the path of destruction," as they were prone to say. María Cristina seldom read newspapers nor did she own a television set and the only radio she listened to was the program she was hearing now, but she had a fine memory and was very aware of the state of things in general. Hadn't World War Two been a small taste of Hell? she asked. Atomic bombs were blown with greater frequency in some parts of the world. An evil empire called Russia was enslaving nations, suppressing freedom and destroying holy churches. Famine in Africa. Revolutions in South America. Earthquakes, tidal waves, volcanic eruptions and floods everywhere! And on the streets of New York, marauding gangs, thieves, cutthroats, drug addicts and more gays, lesbians and whores than in all of Hades. She didn't know who had started this rumor, but she believed it. She accepted it. God, in his infinite wisdom, was about to gather all his true truth believers soon and separate them from those who were about to perish into eternal oblivion.

Here 1960 was almost eight months old, and nothing had happened. When a tipsy Luz Castro asked her why it was that the world was still intact after all that had been said and written and preached, María Cristina replied, "The year is not over."

"I am the Alpha and the Omega," says the Lord God, "who is, and who was, and who is to come, the Almighty."

She opened her eyes and turned around. The aches were gone, except those in her head and eyes. Her hands and feet felt cold. And a strange numbness which ran throughout her body nearly froze her where she sat. But she rose slowly, dragged her chair a few feet and sat down in front of the altar.

"I turned around to see the voice that was speaking to me."

"Lord," María Cristina whispered with closed eyes, "is it you?"

"His head and hair were as white as snow, and His eyes were

like blazing fire."

"Forgive this old woman, for I sinned long ago," she supplicated with clasped hands as she stared at the objects of her veneration. "Now I am your servant, I believe in your Son, I believe in the Word." She beseeched the Lord for a sign to show her the rumor was true and she begged to be saved if so. She struck a wooden match stick and lit a large white candle with it. To her amazement, it melted down to its base in seconds! Dazzled and speechless, she kneeled for over an hour with her eyes closed until she keeled to one side and fell on the wooden floor in a swoon, clenching a black and gold crucifix. A while later, when she had come to, she got up, sat down again and stared at her many saints, pictures and candles, and whispered soft words of prayer in the solitude of her blessed chamber.

Mesmerized and still staring at the little heaven on her altar, María Cristina jumped up when she heard someone knocking rapidly on her door. She got up and asked who it was. René replied that it was he and she let him in. She was surprised to see him enter when she asked him to because he had never set foot inside her home. René disliked María Cristina with an intensity that was impossible to hide. She felt René's chill because he always managed to slip out of his home whenever she dropped by for a chat with his mother. Almost daily. René always remained silent, sat on his cot looking out the window, reading a comic book or staring at the black and white television screen without paying any attention to its images or the boring, weird old lady who lived next door. He always answered her insipid questions—mostly about his ruffian friends or loose girlfriends—with a shrug, nod, or a one- or two-word sentence.

María Cristina almost always sat by the kitchen table where she could speak to Amanda while Amanda did kitchen chores. As María Cristina spoke she always spread small amounts of sugar on the table and pulverized them with her right thumb nail, going over each grain slowly as if her hand were a rolling pin. Sometimes when René entered the kitchen for a glass of water or soda, her hands caught his eyes, and he would stare at them and listened to her words as if hypnotized. She often spoke about the good things that were being done by the church in the neighborhood. Fewer people went hungry in the barrios of Nueva York, and many junkies were sent to the country to be cured. She always ended their chats by inviting Amanda to church, "before it's too late." Amanda shrugged her shoulders.

Once, when René was around nine years old, he sat in the middle of the room looking at a colorful picture of the Virgin Mary that was printed on the front page of the magazine section of the Sunday *Daily News*. María Cristina was walking towards the door after talking to Amanda. René took a pair of scissors and slowly cut the picture into dozens of tiny pieces, as he had done many times while constructing paper figures in school. He loved constructing paper airplanes and butterflies and throwing them into the air or out the window. María Cristina stopped in front of him and looked down at him with the angriest stare he had ever seen in his short life. "René," she whispered hard at him with her face just inches away from his, "you must pray very, very hard for forgiveness for what you have done! If you don't, you will be punished by the Lord until you cry in pain. And afterwards your soul will burn in Hell for what you have done. Pray, pray and ask the Virgin for mercy!" She walked out of the apartment, slamming the door behind her.

He tossed and turned in his sleep for days and repeated a few words of prayer his mother had taught him when he was just barely out of the cradle. He also crossed himself several times a day. Not wishing anyone to know about his transgression, he hid in his mother's closet to pray. Inside, it was crammed with clothes and odds and ends, but there was enough room on its floor for him to kneel. Perhaps here his low voice might be heard by those mysterious beings that lived in the other world.

One day the closet door lock snapped shut, trapping him in. He found himself falling into the darkness of a bottomless pit. Falling, falling until he yelled out. But no one heard him. His mother had gone out somewhere. In his panic, he kicked the door with all his might and broke the lock open. Light poured inside and he made his escape, cursing the day María Cristina Cruz had moved into 113. However, he continued his vigil outside the closet for several more days, repeating the words "perdón,

perdón mi Santa Virgen," until something happened that made him stop. While swinging a wooden broom stick that he used for playing stickball, he accidentally knocked over a plaster figurine of a saint that rested on the mantelpiece. It fell with a loud crash and shattered into dozens of tiny fragments. He looked down on the floor and noticed that it was made of the same plaster as that on the walls and ceiling. A long silence followed and nothing happened. He quickly swept the pieces into a metal dustpan and threw them out the back window, just below María Cristina's window. Then he went out with his stick to play in the street, laughing as he ran down the block.

As he stood in the middle of the dim room, René remembered that day as if it had occurred just moments ago. He looked at the many candles that burned in glass jars beneath the tiny feet of María Cristina's favorite saints. Saint Barbara, Saint John the Divine, Saint Mary and someone she called La Virgen Milagrosa (the Miraculous Virgen) stood there among her statuettes. He felt a sudden urge to swing a stick across the altar, even if he'd burn in hell. The candles cast shadows on the white draped table and walls as the lights danced endlessly in every corner of the room and penetrated parts of the kitchen area. The room had a strong smell of burnt paraffin that lent a staleness to an already stuffy place.

"Remember the height from which you have fallen! Repent and do the things you did first."

The old woman looked strange to René. She wore a long black skirt and red blouse adorned with geometric patterns of various colors. And the look on her face, blank, stiff and as pale as a sheet, confused him. She stared at him for a long time. The lights in back of her created a glow around her that startled him. René felt as if he had just walked into the basement with its many dark corners and pillars that looked like ghostly figures. She barely reached five feet, had straight shoulder-length gray hair that she brushed and tied into a neat bun at the back of her head. Her plain face was always pale, free of makeup or those stylish plucked eyebrows that came to sharp ends. Despite her age, her face was free of wrinkles and was highlighted by a pair of small round eyes that had just a tinge of sadness about them. Under her left eye she had a long and thin dark brown birthmark that looked like a tear. This too she believed was a symbol of her lifelong pains.

"Yes, René?"

"María Cristina, I have somethin' for you."

"Something?"

"Yeah," he answered as he pulled the kerchief out of his shirt.

"Thees, for me? Why?"

"I sell things now. You can have it for just a few bucks."

"You know my English not too goot, but what's a few 'bucks'?"

"How 'bout five dollars. I need da bread."

"Bucks! Bread! Wha' you talkeen 'bout? Take it back. You prob'ly stole it. I know you, you little sinner."

"No, I swear ... "

"Don't swear!"

"Repent!" roared the radio preacher.

"It's imported from India."

"Repent!"

"I don't care if it's imported from India," she said taking the kerchief and switching to Spanish. She remembered something and lowered her voice. "I have something more important to tell you."

She turned her back and walked towards her altar. She placed the kerchief over her head and tied it beneath her chin.

"Come over here, René. I want to show you something miraculous."

He took a few steps forward and stood beside her, not knowing what the old woman was up to. He feared that she was about to go into one of her holy tirades, when all he wanted was to collect the money and leave.

"René, it's not too late to repent ... "

"Please, María Cristina ... "

"No, listen: I am among the elect. I've been warning people for a long time that the end is near, you know that. Now I'm convinced that the time has come at last. He's appointed me his messenger. Look at this tear." She ran a bony index finger down her cheek. "It's a divine sign no one else has. Save yourself, my boy. Look! See! Open your eyes and see the truth! The end is near!" She yelled, cackled, then knelt before her altar, just inches from a large burning candle.

"The angel said to me, 'These words are trustworthy and true. The Lord, the God of the spirits of the prophets, sent his angel to show his servants the things that must soon take place.'"

René looked down at the altar and saw a saucer with the hardened stump of a candle stick. It reminded him of a dead volcano, cold and silent, with the remnants of lava surrounding its base. A sense of weariness overtook him, and he took a step back. But María Cristina continued her harangue until he couldn't take it anymore.

"María!" he yelled, "Stop this shit! All this means nothing to me, nothing! It's all in your mind. Go to a hospital. Go out, anywhere. You're nuts." He grabbed the doorknob.

"No. You're wrong. You are damned. Listen to me ... "

"No. Keep the damn kerchief. It's free. I don't want nothing for it," he yelled nervously and walked out, leaving her still kneeling and supplicating.

"Outside are the dogs, those who practice magic arts, the sexually immoral, the murderers, the idolaters and everyone who loves and practices falsehood." The radio voice faded behind María Cristina's closed door.

René breathed hard, leaning against the wall between his door and María Cristina's. Then he heard the loud and joyful music still coming from Luz Castro's room. She was singing the words to a happy tune she was playing. He ran up the stairs.

SEVEN

"Hi, René. Come in," Luz said as she opened her door and let him in. "Is everything okay? You look like you just came from Hell." He was gasping for air, his face streamed with perspiration.

"Yeah, I'm okay. I jus' ran up da stairs."

"You're a big, strong guy now. You can take it. Sit down and relax."

She closed the door and turned its lock, then led him to a long sectional sofa behind the door. He sat down and felt its soft comfort sooth his sore back. The sofa resembled an inverted L with its small end pointing left, touching the entrance to Luz's kitchen. It was decorated with red and white flowers and thick tree branches on a dark blue background. An end table with a large lamp pressed against its right end. Facing the sofa, to the right of the artificial fireplace, was a wooden bookshelf filled with magazines, several marine artifacts, such as small bells and ship anchors, and many porcelain and glass figurines of animals and ships. A long coffee table; a high-riser divan drawn across the front window, a portable television at its foot and a large wooden record player were all her furnishings, besides a kitchen table in the kitchenette. On her mantelpiece was a row of liquor bottles, some full, some half empty, several wide-mouth wine decanters filled with water or soil and a row of inverted drinking glasses. The decanters contained red and green plants which overflowed their rims and hung down the sides and front of the mantelpiece like drooping vines.

"You okay?" she asked again.

"Yeah, Luz. I jus' wanna take it easy. I got lots'a things on my mind."

"You wanna tell me about it?"

"No, it's okay. But, well, I jus' came from María Cristina's place and she upset me. She's weird, man."

74

"Weird, tell me about it," Luz said matter-of-factly.

"Well, I don't wanna go into it, but she scared da shit outta me wid dis stuff about da world ending soon and people like me and you burning in Hell for our sins. You know da kind'a scary things they always talk about in church an' in almos' every street corner, 'specially on Sundays. You seen dem guys with suits an' Bibles an' American flags, and ladies wid no makeup an' white blouses an' black skirts."

"You really believe in all that, René?"

He shrugged his shoulders.

"That ole lady is nuts. Besides, ain't you a little suspicious?"

"About what?" asked René.

"All this stuff about the world coming to an end? It's the same ole story year in and year out, century after century. He is coming! He is coming! And nothing happens. Me, I don't care. I'll worry about that when the time comes." Luz pointed her right thumb and tapped her chest several times, "If God didn't want us to feel good and do little bad things once in a while, he wouldn't have given us the urge to feel the way we do, right? Besides, all old people are religious. Me and you'll prob'ly do the same when we're old and gray—in case it's true."

"By den I'll be playing a harp in Heaven."

"Or shoveling coal in Hell."

"How you know?"

"I'll be there to open the door of the furnace for you. Anyway, forget it, Papito, it ain't worth getting upset about. Here ... "

She reached out and pulled a white handkerchief from the sofa's end table and wiped his face with it. René inhaled deeply and relished its deep perfume. She smelled the same way, the sofa, the walls. It was a rich flowery aroma that relaxed and excited him. No perfume shop sold it, no garden on a windy day ever bore this scent to him. Gone was the vision of María Cristina Cruz standing before her bright altar, cursing him and worshiping wax, framed cartoons of bleeding saints with eyes forever looking skyward and painted plaster. He leaned back and looked up at the ceiling.

"That's nice. You look better now," she told him. He smiled halfheartedly but said nothing. She went to the kitchen and cracked some ice cubes from an ice tray into a couple of empty glasses.

Speaking louder as she worked, she told René he had to learn to ignore nuts like María Cristina and that strange old man who lived next to her. Luz placed the glasses on the mantelpiece and flipped the stack of 78 RPM records to their reverse sides. Pérez Prado's silvery trumpet was followed by a nostalgic *bolero* sung by Felipe Rodríguez. "La última copa que tomé contigo ... " he crooned as Luz mixed two rum-n-cokes from the bottles on the mantelpiece. She sat down next to René. Her right thigh pressed against his leg. Luz wore a white blouse buttoned in front and a short, thin skirt, tight around the hips, two or so inches above her knees. It was beige and adorned with black roses. "Take this. I'm sure you'll like it."

"Thanks."

"Maybe this will take my headache away. Me and your mother wen' out las' night, remember? I drank and danced so much I had to sleep most of the day. I feel fine now, but my night was spoiled by this jerk I met at the club."

"What'd he do?"

"Nothing, except take his prick out in the middle of the street, right in front of this building, just because I wouldn't let him come up. It would've been okay if he wasn't so high and acted so stupid and desperate. He really surprised me. Some gent!"

"Creep. Dat's really weird."

"Weird? No, just desperate. I had the feeling that he'd been alone a long time—you know, no woman and all that. Then he started pleading with me again to let him come up. I really wanted to, but he changed so fast he threw me off. A different man from the one I met at the Caribe Palace. A girl can't walk with a guy now-a-days without him thinking that she wants to go to bed with him. Especially if you ask him to walk you home. Damn. He grabbed me by the hips, but I hit him with my purse. 'You fucken cockteasing bitch!' he said as he zipped himself. Then I ran up the stairs and locked myself in."

"What a creep," René repeated.

"I should be used to it, but I'm not. He thought I was easy, but I ain't. I know what I like when I see it." She smiled at René and sipped her drink slowly.

As she leaned back he inhaled her soapy freshness and remembered the way she'd excited him earlier in her skimpy shorts. Several times he'd dreamt about her and awakened in the morning with soaked briefs. She dropped by every day as she walked in and out of 113, Amanda's door being just three feet from the building entrance. Sometimes she came in early in the morning while René still lay in bed. He always watched her as she walked around, talking to his mother. Luz had a way of leaning against things and arching her body in a way that made every curve in her full figure seem carved of pure marble, but pulsing with color and life. She always folded her arms beneath her breasts over the kitchen table, or rested her elbows against a sofa-chair until diamond shaped gaps formed between the buttons in her blouse, allowing him a view of her breasts or belly. Always braless, she sometimes wore a tight pullover beige blouse that seemed invisible. And often were the times when she lay on the sofa faced down or on her side, resting or dozing while he looked on with a longing to get down on his knees before her resting form and bury his face between her thighs. This, his friends told him, was what a man was supposed to do.

"I got somethin' to sell you, Luz. Dis little star will bring you good luck. You can have it for a few bucks. Wear it any time, any place. It'll bring nice guys to you an' keep weirdos away. It'll also make you look prettier," René said unbuttoning his shirt. She moved closer to him and stared at the strange object, as if it had just fallen from the sky. Her breasts pressed his bare arms. He breathed deeply and wished that she'd never move away from him.

"It's nice, but I don't need a good luck piece to meet men. I already know too many. Besides, ain't I pretty enough? Where'd you get it, anyway?"

"I found it in an ole abandoned building near Secon' Av'nue. Don't tell Mom. I'm saving money to buy her a present or send her to P.R. Maybe in da future we could move dare. I'm sick of dis block." He gulped down the rest of his drink with a loud swallow, then coughed as the liquor burned its way down his throat.

"Hey man, don't you know how to drink? You suppose to drink slowly, like this." She sipped slowly, then licked the corners of her lips. "It's nice and cool." She got up and mixed two more drinks. "Want da star?"

"Maybe. But I don't like fancy things. Besides, you won't get much money selling little things like that out on the street. Find work somewhere, you're a grown man already, René. I bet you smoke pot and screw girls."

"I hate da smell of pot—burning horse shit smells better. I think about girls all da time, even when I sleep."

"I bet you do, otherwise somethin's wrong."

"You ever bin in love?"

"Just once, but I'll never forget it, though I really want to. It almost drove me to the nut house. Ay, how I loved that man! He was married, but I didn't care. For nine years I tended to him and his needs. I didn't care if there was another woman in his life because I knew that I was the one he always cared for. The only one he truly loved. Or so he said. Then one day he vanished, scramed outta sight. I didn't know where at first, but I found out soon enough. Florida. Yeah, I followed him all the way down there to that land of crocodiles and Cubans. And when I finally caught up to him, he said that his family was more important to him than anything or anyone else in the world. Imagine! After all those years, he comes up with this shit! Then he said that reading the gospel and bowling with his wife and kids brought him closer to her and earned him salvation. Salvation! That fuckin' cunt-eating, drunken liar! Man!" She now stood in front of René with arms akimbo. "He no longer wished to see me. 'How dare you lower yourself and tail me so many miles,' he said, then added, 'If Mary Magdalena was forgiven her sins, then you too could be saved.'" Luz lowered her voice until it was almost a whisper.

René remained silent, sipping his drink, trying to understand her sad story. Love was something he heard about constantly, but the more he heard, the more confused he became. It was something one was supposed to feel always but almost impossible to find. He had seen love bring some people together and place others in early graves.

"I donno what love is," he said looking blankly at the floor.

"Love is temporary insanity," she said as she jingled the ice cubes in her drink with the tip of her right index finger. She placed it between her rosy lips and sucked it dry. "How I loved that man! We danced together, ate the same foods, went everywhere together without being afraid of being seen walking hand in hand into a club, park or beach. Even our thoughts were the same. Whenever he said something, I'd say, 'I was just thinking about that,' and he'd say the same thing whenever I reflected what was on his mind. He sang sweet songs to me while making love. Then that wife-bitch took him away and filled his head with all that Bible stuff. I'm sick of all those hypocrites who call me a sinner and pray before and after screwing: 'Oh God, help me come, bring us a baby. I'm coming, I'm coming, oh God!' I love joy and I don't regret it. God gave us our bodies to love and enjoy. I swore never to love again. Because of him, I turned into a whore."

Luz pulled René by the hand and led him to the middle of the floor. Tito Puente's mellow voice filled the room as he sang a sad bolero about a long lost love. Luz and René danced in small circles, cheek to cheek, breast to breast, hips almost inseparable.

"You're not a whore, Luz. I like you more dan you think."

She smiled and pressed her head against the right side of his. A bit awkward at first René followed Luz's lead as she pulled him towards her, backwards, sideways, round and round. It reminded him of the many "grinds," slow dances, he enjoyed with the girls of East Harlem on Saturday nights in social clubs or dimly lit apartments. But Luz was a real woman, one who could take him into that dark cavern that was every woman, a secret place filled with things precious and of endless ecstasy. He inhaled the rain-fresh fragrance in her black hair, a scent that was strange, yet familiar. Their closeness soon aroused an intense excitement in him that embarrassed him as if he were dancing with someone new. Braless, her full breasts hung in loose splendor and pressed against his chest, their hard nipples touching his. Her thighs were supple, long and squeezed against his legs and croch. She felt his hardness and withdrew her head a bit, then arched it back further until her hair hung straight down. She smiled at him through her dark, narrow eyes. He felt a bit nervous and pulled back a bit.

"Relax, Papi, ain't you ever done it before?" she whispered.

René shook his head slowly, and took another long deep breath, eyes a bit downcast. She pressed closer until they touched once again. Now he thought of Luz only and forgot she was his mother's friend and where he was. All voices and sounds in the apartment and outside were lost in the invisible atmosphere that surrounded him and this fabulous woman. They twirled in circles, sliding along her slippery floor. He buried his face in her neck and chest and inhaled her natural fragrance, tasted her salty bronze skin and touched her between her legs. Luz sucked her breath between clenched teeth and whispered, "Ay Papi," in his ear. She touched him and he felt an urge to come, but he held back. She lowered the window shade and turned off the ceiling lights, then switched on the lamp near the sofa. They were near the highriser bed, and she pushed him gently until they were laying down, she on top of him, removing his clothes slowly with delicate movements. He reached up as he lay naked and fumbled with her blouse.

"Easy, baby. Here, let me show you." She took his moist hands and unbuttoned her blouse, then slipped out of her skirt. In that semi-dark room, directly above his own bed, he breathed deeply and sucked in his breath when he heard the soft ripple of her panties as they slipped down her buttocks and legs, revealing her thick bushy mound and wide hips. Luz was more voluptuous than he had imagined. The very touch of her warm, smooth body pressing against his made his heart race. He ran his palms up and down her body. She was very hairy and moist between her legs. He closed his eyes when he felt her lips and teeth pressed against his nipples.

"You're a pretty girl, Luz."

"I'm a woman, not a girl."

"Ay, Mami!"

"Silly," she laughed. "You're gorgeous."

She kissed his face, licked his neck and chin, and swallowed his erection. He held on and drank the sweet nectar that oozed from every pore of her firm body, kissed and licked her between her legs as he'd dreamed about so many times. She straddled him and added a gentle rocking squeak of bedsprings to their motions. Warmed by an ardent desire and summer heat, they inhaled the same breath with long passionate kisses as they rolled to every corner of the bed with an endless play of motions and positions. The music had stopped and the sounds of their whispers and rapid love making filled the room.

"Oh, Luz, Luz, Luz ... " René whispered and gently bit her earlobes.

"Baby, baby. Sing to me, René," Luz whispered in his ear.

"I'm just a lonely boy, lonely and blue … "

"No, silly," she laughed.

Moments later they lay in each other's arms, in the semi darkness of the evening, still kissing, stroking each other and sharing a cool drink. Gone were the unsteady nerves that had made him shake with uncertainty as he made love to this very real woman. Gone was the vision of the old woman and the pitiful way in which she had lived her long, pathetic life. And gone from his sight and thoughts was the noisy, troublesome world beyond the door and windows of Luz Castro's little haven. They repeated their love-making several times until, tired and sleepy, she fell into a deep slumber. René quietly dressed. He ran his hands through her long hair and pushed aside a broad wave that draped her pretty face. So beautiful, so beautiful, he thought as if he'd just met and fallen in love with her. He kissed the palm of her right hand and quietly walked out the door.

He tip-toed down the stairs and stood in front of his door, where he heard his mother speaking and laughing with someone. He entered and found his mother sitting on the sofa, pouring wine into a man's glass.

EIGHT

"René, I'd like you to meet a friend of mine," Amanda said when he entered. "This is Fernando Fuentes."

René gave Fuentes a sidelong glance, nodded a faint hello and went to the kitchen for a glass of water. He smelled of perfume, rum and jasmine. He felt a delicious, yet strange taste in his mouth which excited him. Not wanting Amanda to notice the smell of liquor on his breath or clothes, René quickly dashed across the apartment, said a quick goodbye and turned the doorknob to leave.

She called out to him in a loud voice, though she was just a few feet away. "Sit down for a while."

"I got things to do outside, Mom. Some other time."

"Five minutes," Fuentes said smiling. "I don't bite."

René hesitated, realizing that it was not a good idea to leave his mother alone with this man, regardless of who he might be. He walked to his cot and sat down on its foot end, close to the door entrance. Amanda and Fernando sat on opposite ends of the couch, facing him. Feeling a bit uneasy, René eyed the stranger without real interest. He disliked being obliged to sit and chat with someone outside his circle of relatives and choice friends. Especially people who came from out of nowhere. René was not used to seeing men in the house. His mother was a woman who liked being alone, had few friends, although she knew many people, and rarely brought suitors to the house.

Fuentes looked like a suitor. He dressed like one, wearing a sky-blue suit that looked as if it had been pressed by a steamroller, not a wrinkle in sight. The sailor wore a cologne which smacked René's nostrils and reminded him of a barber shop where toiletries blended with tobacco smoke. Fuentes spoke in a low, gentle tone when addressing Amanda. He smiled as he spoke, which irritated René, had flushed cheeks and agreed with everything she said.

Amanda was always cautious and sensitive to what René might think about her. She seldom felt so relaxed, laughed so much, showed such great interest in someone other than her son. "You're quite a fella, René," Fernando said in a nearly unaccented English. It surprised René, because Fuentes reminded him of a hick. A hick to René was anyone from Puerto Rico who dressed in loud colors or spoke little or no English, even after twenty or thirty years of living in the States.

"Your mother here has nothing but good things to say about you. She's been talking about you for the past half hour."

"Sorry," she said shyly.

"No, please don't. I'm not complaining. It's just that there're so many rotten kids around here, that it's a pleasure to hear something good said about one, at least."

"Mom says nice things 'bout everyone ... "

"Not everyone, René."

"Anyway, I've been to many, many places and known lots people. I know what kind of man I'm dealing with when I meet one." He sat back in the sofa, crossed his legs and cupped his right knee with clenched hands.

"You a Gypsy? Can you read minds?" René said, drawn by the man's swagger.

"No, I'm not and I can't read minds. But, being a sailor teaches you things you can't learn anywhere else but at sea, away from most people." He uncrossed his legs and slid to the sofa's edge. "I can tell that you and me are the same kind of guy. We don't take shit from nobody and we can smell a rat a mile away. Right?" Fuentes spoke with a captious tone.

"Dis one can be a bit too tough at times," Amanda said.

"Yeah, but only sometimes," René said.

"Sometimes, baloney. Sailors are proud guys. I don't peel potatoes and you don't shine shoes, right?"

"What you do on ships?" Amanda asked in a sweet voice.

"Well, a little bit of everything, I guess. Sometimes I assist the boatswain with the rigging, chains, anchor. I also cook. But mostly I work in the hull, where we keep supplies and cargo. Like a watchman, I make sure nobody steals anything. Too many thieves sneak down there. Yup, even on a ship you can't escape the rotten crumbs. They'd steal your teeth if you sleep with your mouth open, and they spot a speck of gold between them."

"When I was a little girl living in Puerto Rico, I used to think dat da island was a giant ship sailing in da middle of da ocean, wid no lan' in sight except our own shores. An' da endless sky wid it's many daylight colors an' million nighttime stars guided us at night."

"Where to?" Fuentes asked.

"I don't know."

"That's quite a picture, I can just see it myself," Fuentes continued. "But, I would call the ship the S.S. Rico. How's that?"

Amanda laughed so long and loud she seemed silly and annoying to René. By the very way she stared at Fuentes, with her bright round eyes and nervous way of shifting her body around the edge of the sofa, René knew that his mother was softening to him or lowering her guard. René was unmoved by Fuentes's bragging or humor, but he listened, occasionally turning his head around to glance out the open window.

"Fernando, tell René about da places you bin to."

"Well, muchacho, I've been a sailor since twelve. Loved every minute of it. Well, you may wonder why, but I don't have a smart answer for you. I will say this: I belong at sea. My blood is as salty as its waters, and its waves carry me and the ship to strange and beautiful places I never dreamed about. New York isn't the entire world. In fact, just a speck on a world atlas."

"Sounds like you read that somewhere," René remarked. Amanda opened her eyes wide and gave René a long, deathly stare.

"René ... "

"No, it's okay Amanda. Maybe I did read it somewhere, or maybe I just made it up. It's how I really feel. Go out there someday and you'll see. Anyway, I love sailing. Most people don't. Planes and cars are more dangerous than ships, I tell you. They say cruising is expensive, monotonous and always sharks just yards below your feet. That's all a lot of baloney." Another laugh from Amanda. "Me, I want to live and enjoy every minute. You never know when your number is coming up." He turned his face to Amanda. "A mariner's work is brutal at times; makes you feel like a mule. Someday I want to be married, take care of a nice wife. Anyway, lots of sailors don't have much to do, so they spend their time hiding in little spots—and there's lots of dark spots on board—sipping rum or playing dice or looking at men's magazines. Me, I don't waste my time. Never waste time, René. I read books. The marquis Donatien Alphonse Francois de Sade, Marx, Nostradamus, Finn MacCool—really great men. You know, most people look at the black ocean at night and are horrified because it looks so bottomless. Many people sink into it, day and night and are never seen again. When I was your age I wasn't afraid of the sea. Sometimes when I'm sailing and a great storm threatens to sink my ship at night, I go on deck just to look at the black face of the sea and smile at her. No sir, I ain't afraid, not me." Fuentes leaned back and rested his right arm above Amanda's shoulder.

Amanda listened in awe as Fuentes unraveled one great yarn after another, always with himself as its hero. She envied his wide experience and his manly courage. Alone and sheltered all her life, she had never traveled more than fifty or so miles from her home, whether in Puerto Rico or New York. As she listened, she day-dreamed and wished that she too had been to all those wonderful places. Exotic countries she had only heard about or seen in movies or photos. She saw Fernando as a brave, intelligent, honest, handsome, man: a perfect hero. He is still a stranger, she thought. Yet, he was a friend of Luz Castro, surely someone trustworthy.

The more Fuentes spoke, the more restless René grew. He wished to escape to the streets and walk in the warm summer night, hang out with the gang, go to the Eagle theater where they played three movies daily. Perhaps he might go out and find another apartment to rob. But, next time he'd steal something valuable. Possibly some real jewelry, cash, something worth selling or trading, instead of the miserable comb, kerchief and star. That junk that had only brought him nightmares, embarrassment and empty pockets. Now he sat listening to one bullshit story after another from a man who'd obviously told the same stories to a hundred women and their two or three hundred offspring.

To René, a real man was brave, yet merciful, cool and always unafraid. A real hero didn't need an audience because he'd be too busy fighting for his life to think about praise and applause. He also noticed that whenever Fuentes spoke about himself, his eyelids opened, and his high forehead aligned with deep wrinkles until he resembled an old rooster with a weathered cockscomb. Fuentes noticed the effect his words had on the attractive widow and continued, often repeating himself, as if he had struck an impressive melody on a piano. He grinned at René, who returned the grin and looked at the merchant marine in apathetic silence. René grew weary after several tales of tempests at sea, trading posts in the middle of the Amazon where the name Fernando Fuentes was known and diamond mines in Africa Fuentes had worked in.

Halfway through an anecdote, Fuentes realized that René had lost interest in him and his exploits. At the end of his tenth tale, a dead silence followed which lasted several long moments. Fuentes switched topics in one breath, hoping to say something the young punk might appreciate.

"Well, René, what you think about the upcoming fight? Think Johansson'll beat Patterson?"

"No way. The champ can't be beat."

"No champ can't be beat."

"Then he ain't no real champ."

"I once saw a fight in Cuba, way before you were born, which shocked me and left me broke. There he was, the welterweight champion, pounding away at this little local guy who looked more like a mouse than a boxer. Round after round the little guy kept dodging, running, jabbing whenever he got trapped against the ropes or in a corner."

That did it. At last, here was the clincher that grabbed René's attention. Fuentes spoke rapidly, got up several times, shadow-boxed as he described the action, punching and jabbing the air, covering up, stepping forward, sideways, backwards.

Amanda smiled, excited, as if she had been there in Cuba along-side of him, watching the mighty struggle with him.

" . . . then, in the semi-final round the champ gave the challenger a left uppercut to the jaw. Down he went, but he sprang up from the canvas like a rabbit out of a hole after three counts. The champion chased him to a corner and was about to attack again when the bell rang. You'll never believe what happened in the last round."

"What?" René asked.

"What?" Amanda echoed.

"The little guy hit the champ with a lucky shot to the chin that came from out of nowhere and down he went. He got up exhausted, from all the punches he'd thrown—maybe three hundred—and feeling dizzy. He was pounded by the runt and knocked out."

"How much money you loose?" Amanda asked.

"Five hundred pesos. Tough little guy. I didn't think he had it in him. What a shock."

"Thing's like dat don't happen in real life," René said as he got up to leave. The sailor looked so clownish shadow-boxing in his suit that René was convinced he was as harmless as any Bozo. Mother was safe.

"René! If Fernando says it's true, den it's true."

"Doesn't happen often, but it does," Fuentes said sitting back.

René said goodbye despite Amanda's protests.

"It's okay, I don't mind," Fuentes said in Spanish when they were alone again. "That son of yours is nice, but he lacks manners."

"He's a good boy growing up too fast. You know how teenagers are."

"I'm sure you're a wonderful mother, but you live in New York. Kids are different here. I grew up in Puerto Rico and respected my elders. I listened to them and did as I was told without question or argument. Sounds old fashion, but it's good. Still, I like him. He just needs a grown man to show him the ways of life. And I may be good for him; boys need a man they can look up to. I'll be a good friend and teach him all I know."

"I'm sorry. He's moody and doesn't trust everybody. I try raising him as well as I can, but like other kids, he picks up too many bad habits from the streets. He doesn't talk about what he does outside, but I know he's okay. Don't worry, I know how to handle him. I'm not a man, but I'm strong enough to keep him in place. He didn't mean to run out like that. You tell wonderful true stories. Look, he gave me this comb he found in a back yard."

She removed the hairpiece from her head, letting loose a long wave of hair which cascaded down to her shoulders. Fuentes stared at her as she brushed her hair into place using her cupped hands.

The smooth ends of her hair touched her bare shoulders. He grew so excited and confident that he reached out to touch her. He was about to run his hands along her hair, perhaps touch her shoulder, but he stopped short, as if paralyzed, when he recognized the silver comb. The only one of its kind, he was told when he bought it in a shop in Hong Kong. He was convinced it was the only one of it's kind, because the jeweler had used the very same shiny mercury-head dimes that Fuentes had given him to weld. They were dated dimes that he'd won from a collector during a dice game. He polished the comb very frequently until it glittered even in dim light. This had to be the same silver comb.

"Let me see it." Fuentes took the comb and looked at it carefully. Yes, it's end teeth were missing and their stumps carefully filed; it's half circle almost looked like a U from being stored beneath heavy objects too long. They were all dated consecutively: 1920, 1921, 22 ... And on the inside curvature, barely visible, were the italicized initials F.A.F., less than a quarter inch high.

"Very nice, Amanda. Tell me something, did he give you anything else?"

"Like what?"

"Oh, nothing in particular. Just curious, it's such a rare piece I thought he might have given you other nice things. What a good kid! But listen, I really have to get going. I've got something very important to do that slipped my mind."

She noticed the sudden change and the quick way he got up from his seat, but said nothing except thanks, goodbye and come again as she walked him to the door and locked it after him.

Fuentes quickly skipped down the front steps of 113 looking left and right towards both ends of the street, searching for René. He found him in front of the fire hydrant near Park, in front of the garden, sipping cold water and splashing some on his warm face. When René opened his burning eyes he saw Fuentes standing in front of him with a deadpan stare that chilled him.

"René, I gotta talk to you. Let's go for a walk."

"What you want? I talked to you already."

"Come on kid, your mom is my friend. I wanna be your friend too. Trust me."

"I got too much friends already. I don't want more."

"Come on, kid. I just wanna ask you something in private. I can't talk business in the middle of the street in front of all these people. Just you and me."

Perhaps it was the word business or it may have been Fuentes's attempt at being a nice guy, or René simply bore in mind that this guy had really done nothing wrong to him. Besides, Fuentes was his mother's friend. In any case, he followed the sailor up and along Park Avenue, then turned left after a long, silent while. They entered one of the dark pedestrian tunnels beneath the train tracks and were about half-way through when Fuentes suddenly grabbed René with such powerful force that it almost left him breathless and slammed him against the bare granite wall. Water ran down its sides and soaked his back, but the pain was nothing compared to the horror he felt when Fuentes placed the sharp end of a switchblade on his neck, enough for him to feel the needle sting of its deathly menace.

"You fucken little stealing rat! Think you could get away with stealing my things, eh?"

"No! Lemme go! I didn't steal nothin' from you!"

"You gave your mother that silver comb with its dimes, didn't you! It's the only one of its kind. It's mine. Where's the rest of the stuff?"

"What stuff?"

"You know, the kerchief, the star and all my money?"

"Money! What money?" René yelled trembling and feeling the blade pricking his neck deeper.

"The money you stole?"

"I took no money."

"So, you were the one."

"I took no money."

"That was the third time this month they robbed my place."

"It wasn't me."

"Maybe, but you did steal my stuff and you're gonna pay. If you don't do as I say, I'll push this knife in until you feel its handle. I've killed guys for giving me the evil eye or double crossing me. One less rat in the barrio won't be missed."

Too stunned to speak, René remained still, in a silent stupor. His heart raced and he felt a hard pulsing in his temples. This was followed by a sudden chill as Fuentes removed the knife, folded it until it clicked shut and placed it in his jacket pocket before anyone walked by. In a few eternal seconds René felt as if he'd just skipped over his own grave.

"You lack manners, *m'ijo*. Wise up," Fuentes remarked.

René said nothing.

"Now listen, you little scum-bag. Meet me here the day after tomorrow around twelve noon. I have a little job for you. Maybe I'll give you a few bucks after you pay back what you owe me. I want you to deliver something for me, okay?"

René nodded slowly.

"Go on. Your mother may be looking for you."

René ran out of the tunnel and down Park as fast as he could. He remembered his bad dream and wished he could wake up. But he knew he was awake and the phantom had caught up with him.

NINE

The following day, shortly before noon, René sat pensive beneath the cool shade of the ailanthus tree which towered over the garden fence and hung loosely over the gray pavement. He leaned back and felt the wire mesh pressing against his skin, but his pain was far deeper. Except for an occasional car that whisked by, the block was deserted. It was turning into another warm day and the sky, blue as the Caribbean Sea near a shore, seemed as if someone had cut it with a sharp sword, it was so spotless and clear. René looked up and around but saw nothing. He felt that he had entered a battlefield in which words and shocking deeds were bullets and weapons. Life was an endless war. Like a soldier facing an awesome foe, the struggle was futile. Who could he turn to, he asked himself, and how could he get rid of this goon who wanted to kill him and seduce his mother. The shock of sudden surprise was something new to him. No longer could he go slinking around East Harlem at odd hours, filling his pockets and shirt without being caught and punished severely. To make matters worse, he now saw that he was in contact with a man who was not only stealing his mother's affection, but one who was also capable of killing. Everything was happening too fast.

The more he thought about it, the less he blamed himself for all the trouble and soon realized that this fucken mess was all Mom's fault. After all, she was the one who met the creep and brought him home. She should have stayed home, where she belonged, and dated a real gentleman. A friend of the family, perhaps, or one of those nice guys that wore suits on Sundays, went to church and loved his mother. Lots of them guys around. On the other hand, some of those cats could be just as horny and dangerous as Fuentes. Except that Fuentes had that deceptive look about him: he smirked, seemed too happy, friendly and nice. A man like him could fool the most perceptive man and the most vulnerable woman.

Above him the overhead rails rattled as a passing train sped by at full speed, heading somewhere south. René wished that he could jump on it and travel wherever it was going. New Jersey, Virginia, Florida; pink, yellow, red colors on a map came alive in his mind as he envisioned himself speeding past lush countryside and mountains he had never seen. In Key West he would sail the blue waters of the Caribbean Sea, then perhaps live in the deep the heart of Puerto Rico. And all this time his mother would be by his side, free of ogres, ready to shelter and protect him.

He thought about his father in moments like these and whished that he had met him. He must have been a great guy, one who could drink, work, love and fight his way out of the meanest battle, with fists, bullets or machete, as real *jíbaros* do in the country. All that was left was a faint blur, a stoneface of a man with gentle eyes and a voice that soothed him when he was barely two. His father's voice could crack the air with one mighty shout. And like his old man, René wasn't about to let anyone push him around. What would his father, shadow that he was, think if he knew that a Gómez would turn tail at the slightest hint of danger. Then again, too many butchered bodies were found in dark alleys in East Harlem and floating along the city's rivers.

He looked up when he sensed someone standing in front of him. Fuentes looked down at René, told him to rise and led him into a granite passageway.

"Listen, guppy, take this package to the Friendly Bar and Grill on Brooke Avenue, in the Bronx. Tell the bartender it's from Meduso and do as she says."

Dressed sharply once again in a new suit and bathed with enough cologne to fumigate a squad of flies, Fuentes managed to stay cool despite the intense heat. As he reluctantly took the package, René wondered if the sailor was unaffected by heat.

"What's in it?"

"Never mind. They're Indian plants. Go on, here." He handed René two quarters for subway tokens, then sauntered off along Park as René headed towards Lexington.

Alone at home later that afternoon, Amanda sat across her cot with her back against the wall, deeply absorbed in the middle of a pulp novel. It was her favorite way of escaping into a dream world where anything was possible. It was a world where a woman like her could be rescued from misery by a perfect man. Although she had quit high school within six months of the first year in order to support herself, she had developed a passion for reading novels and pulp fiction to wile away the empty hours. Before coming to New York, she had spent hours pouring over exotic tales set in distant jungles and strange hidden cities while rocking herself in the cool shade of her front porch in her wooden house in Santurce. She loved trading those popular softbound Latino novels with her neighbors and delighted in showing off her familiarity and knowledge of scribblers such as Hortencia Pimpinela De Bonbón Y Bonbón, Agapito Isople and Don Pluto Frío. She once found a coverless Spanish translation of Gustave Flaubert's *Madame Bovary* in an abandoned schoolhouse, but hated the heroine from the start. The author was too detached, and Emma Bovary lacked moral strength. Besides, Amanda concluded, a woman should always know her place. She returned the naked book to the empty schoolhouse.

Here in New York, she discovered to her delight an endless supply of *novelas* written in wonderful Spanish! There were tales of swooning *doñas* in Spain forever lamenting their soldier lovers going off to war, Aztec princesses rescued from the clutches of evil sorcerers, and always that reliable saga of the wealthy South American family with its myriad of screwing cousins, lost uncles, greedy patriarchs, sacrificing wives, playboys, whores, thieves, ex-cons, bastards, vagabond virgins and always a debauching army colonel or general festooned with gorgeous regalia who sent young men to early graves at the slightest whim. She read twice as much as she had on the island. Here there was more time, more books, more reasons for escape. After René left, she quickly turned to a special tale that drew her strongly.

The *novela*, titled *Una Dama Amada*, centered around a poor country girl somewhere in the South American wilds who falls in love with a hunter who is strangled by a boa snake three months after their honeymoon. She finds it impossible to love again. Ten years later, she meets another hunter who wears necklaces made of panther fangs and dons rawhide garb. He has a handsome face, but not as handsome as her late husband. He nevertheless woos her despite her strong, chaste resistance. She feels safe and comfortable with him. He tells her stories of his fortunes and misfortunes and makes her laugh with pantomimes and impersonations of movie stars. One day while huddled under a huge tree during a heavy rain storm, she succumbs to his pleadings. The scene was so intense and passionate that Amanda nearly slipped off the cot's edge.

She closed the book and lay down, facing the ceiling. She breathed deeply, pressed the book against her heaving breasts and bit her lower lip. Lately she had tried to avoid reading novels that aroused strong, sometimes overwhelming, desires she could find no outlet for, but it was difficult. Their covers were usually illustrated with half-naked couples locked in an embrace that could only be broken by a team of wild horses.

Amanda remembered Fernando Fuentes and allowed his image to enter her thoughts. How strange, she said to herself, that after so many years of rejecting the advances of so many men that one should suddenly come out of nowhere—literally nowhere—and match her paper heroes. And it had happened so quickly. The more she recalled the night they met the greater it became until, lost in a dream, she saw the night as a perfect scene in a drama too beautiful and too real and unmatched in any book or stage she had ever read or viewed. His words, his manners, his face, his voice with its deep manly resonance, his spirit and his passion for books convinced her that at last, at long last, her barren days were numbered. She also recalled the many countless disappointments she had had in the past and quickly asked if such a man, as Fuentes purported to be, did really exist? She was older now and knew more about life than when she roamed the narrow streets of Puerto Rico's pueblos as a spirited girl seeking fun and excitement.

A sudden, loud knock on the door aroused her from her muddled thoughts. She quickly placed the novel aside and walked to the door.

"Hello, I'm sorry for knocking so loud," Fuentes said. He stood in the doorway with a bouquet of white and pink hedge flowers in his right hand. "I couldn't call you because you have no phone. Just passing by and thought I'd say hello. Is it all right?"

"Sure," she replied with sleepy eyes and tired voice, "come in."

"Here, these flowers are for you. Lovely flowers for a lovely lady."

"Thank you," she said and put the flowers in a metal vase, filled it with cold water and placed it on the coffee table in front of the sofa. "Tell me something, Fernando. Are you married?"

"Married? Me? Would I be here with you? Why do you ask?"

"Well, you know what they say about sailors ... "

"That's only in songs and gossip. Most things they say about us isn't true. Once, before I joined the merchant marines, I heard that a man had been swallowed by a whale and lived to tell about it! Imagine someone believing something so crazy. I guess people believe what they want to believe. No, I'm not married. I was once, but that was long ago, in another country." She stared at him, surprised that he was searching for words. Sensing she had invoked a painful memory in him, she tried to draw back.

"You don't have to tell me ... " she started to say, but he cut her off and said that it was all right.

"We met somewhere in Mexico. I don't recall where exactly, those small villages there are like the ones in Puerto Rico. You know, they all look the same: small houses, dirt roads. Anyway, she was alone in the world with no one to help her. Poor, hungry, but very pretty and loving. She was always there waiting for me no matter how long I was gone away. Always greeted me warmly and never betrayed me. I know she didn't because I never betrayed her, 'though I had many chances. I loved her that much." He reached out as he spoke and stroked the petals of the flowers with a gentleness that surprised Amanda. "One day she couldn't stand the thought of me going away again and she went after me, just as the ship I was sailing on took off. The weather was bad, a heavy rain and strong wind hid her screams as she tried to jump on board, but fell into the harbor instead. This I found out when I returned. I haven't loved another woman since then. I believe in love. None of that woman-in-every-port business for me."

A long silence followed, broken only by the sounds of the street. She got up and offered him a drink.

"No, thanks. Maybe later. Could you put on the radio or something?"

"Sure."

She got up and turned the plastic knob of her old Victrola left and right and stopped suddenly when she heard a woman singing a slow, gentle *bolero*, like the ones they played at the Caribe Palace. Fernando gently pulled Amanda by the hand and led her to the middle of the floor. She followed him, reluctant at first, then relaxed as their bodies met in a tight cling. When the number was over, another followed. He held her tight, but she pulled away. Feeling her resistance, Fuentes let her go when he remembered that René could return quickly from his errand to the Bronx. She turned to a wall mirror and started to brush her hair with trembling hands. Her heart raced and she breathed fast, but her eyes couldn't avoid his deep, penetrating stare and warm smile.

"Amanda, I think we should go for a walk. I know it's getting dark out, but Central Park is pretty at night. Lots of people still go out to the garden and north lake. Okay?"

Amanda nodded, and they walked out the door. She looped her right arm through one of his and followed him along the street towards Central Park. Several of her acquaintances saw them and threw her inquiring looks and mischievous smiles. Amanda held her head high, looked straight ahead and walked with a proud step that matched her new man's slow and steady gait; they had all the time in the world.

They entered the park near 106th Street and walked along the lamp-lit road of the garden until they reached the Harlem Meer. They turned left and followed the lake's west bank and continued north. The lake was spotted with couples in small groups in rowboats which cruised slowly to every corner of it. The crowded shore grew dense and spread up several hills as other couples strolled, drawn by a strange, but pleasant music. A chamber orchestra had assembled about halfway up the lake. The musicians sat on wooden folding chairs, reading their music scores, made visible by several bright spotlights, and playing their instruments. Vivaldi's "Summer Concerto" from his "Four Seasons," Purcell's silvery melodies from the "Fairy Queen," and Mozart's "Serenade Number 13" echoed throughout that north-east end of Central Park. They played in a semi-circle at the lakeside which juts out onto the water like a concrete pier. In back of them was a granite wall, perhaps fifty feet high, called "The Mount." On its summit a black iron picket fence and two ancient cannons was all that remained of a Revolutionary War fortress. Several lamp posts illuminated the old fort and shined along the crest of the rock. A conductor wearing a white jacket and black pants now led the players through the andante of J. S. Bach's "Violin Concerto in A Minor."

The music sounded a bit faint to Amanda and Fernando as they continued following the water's edge, but the stone wall created an echo that waved across the lake. They crossed a small foot bridge, turned right and east. They sat on a park bench near a boathouse and diner and watched people walking by chatting or rowing around in circles over the dark waters of the Harlem Meer. From here they could still hear the music coming from the opposite shore. The boathouse restaurant was a large red brick structure shaped like a private house with a slanted tiled roof and shingles. A confusing din escaped through the open doors and windows as loud laughter, shouts, the rattling of pans, dishes and utensils made the music faint, but still audible.

"You like that music?" Fernando asked when he noticed Amanda listening. She smiled and said it sounded nice. They listened and shifted their eyes between the musicians and the people boarding or leaving the leaky, wooden rowboats. Some of them calmly stepped off and jumped on the ribs of the ramp, while others, afraid of getting their shoes and clothes wet, scurried merrily onto dry spots on the ramp. Some boaters were aided by burly men who clasped boats by the nose and pulled them almost halfway up the ramp. New rowers got in and the men pushed the rowboats onto the lake once again. Sometimes Amanda's ears followed the music's increasing tempo and her eyes rested on the dim glow of the fort.

Fernando placed his arm around Amanda and pulled her close to him. She placed her head on his shoulder and looked at the silvery glimmer of the dark lake. "Try not to fall asleep. This music does that to you sometimes," he told her. When the music ended, she clung to his arm as if afraid someone might pull her away into a dark space between hidden trees, never to be seen again. Sometimes she stared at several fireflies which flew by lighting their tails, disappearing, then reappearing once again.

They exited the park at 110th Street and Fifth Avenue and walked north until they reached Fuentes's block. He stopped in front of his building.

"I live here," he said. "Want to come up?"

"Ah, I don't think ... " she stammered.

"Come on, just for a while."

She looked around. "I don't think it's right."

"This is silly. Why are you acting this way? I've been alone with you and visited you without forgetting that I'm a gentleman."

"I can't say, I don't know."

"The last thing I want in this world is to hurt someone so kind and beautiful as you. I've never met anyone else like you." He took her right hand and gently kissed the back of her fingers.

She looked at him and saw in his shiny moist brown eyes a warmth and gentleness that calmed her. As if awakened from an endless dark dream she hesitated, but felt an urge, long dormant, long fought within herself to hold someone close to her. She yearned to feel the hard flesh and warmth of his body next to hers. Loving, kissing this special man that had taken so long to come into her unhappy life. He pulled her gently by the hand, and she followed him into the building.

As Amanda was led up the stairs, a sudden pang of fear chilled her and made her stop half-way up the long, dark staircase. How could she have come this far with a man she barely knew? She made a sudden excuse to turn around and return outside where it was safe, but he begged her not to. She looked around. From downstairs the music from the Ponce Bar and Grill filtered through the floor so loud that it could muffle the loudest scream or struggle. Remembering he was a sailor, she envisioned him routinely climbing these same stairs in the arms of a bar whore. For a second she felt like a whore, herself, about to lay across a squeaky bed in a two-bit room. Why this sudden change of heart? She could not say. Perhaps it was the bar, the popular image of the worldly sailor, or maybe it was the overwhelming feeling that she had known this man a long time and felt comfort, fear, desire almost beyond control. She stood still with one foot firm on the step up.

"Amanda, I'll do anything you say. We could go back if that's

what you really want. Again, I'd like you to know that I wouldn't
do anything in the world to hurt you."

"I ... "

"Relax, *negra*. I can't put into words what I really feel for you.
You're precious, beautiful and a very, very decent woman. If I
didn't think so I wouldn't have invited you to my place. My home,
like yours, is as pure as a spring."

She took a step up and stopped again.

"If you want," he added, "we can leave the door open. Doña
Clara, the landlady, lives on my floor."

When they reached his door, he opened it, snapped a light
switch on the inside wall and asked her to enter. Amanda stood in
the middle of the living room, looking around, reluctant to sit.

"Ah, I almost forgot," Fuentes said. He walked over to a corner,
picked up a flower pot which contained a multi-colored phlox plant
and placed it on a coffee table. He went outside, knocked on a
neighbor's door and returned accompanied by a kindly looking
old woman.

"Doña Clara, here's the plant I promised you. I grew it from
seeds I brought from South America. That's why I took so long in
giving it to you. I wanted it to grow a bit before I gave it to you.
Here." He handed it to her. The old woman looked at Amanda
and smiled as she picked up the vase and walked towards the door.

"Thank you, Don Fernando. You're a good man and a fine
tenant. Treat this nice lady good," she said and placed the palm of
her hand on his face. As she walked out the door, she was about
to close it after her, but Fuentes asked her to leave it open.

A few minutes later, Fernando and Amanda sat on the sofa
chatting over a bottle of chilled white Chablis.

She had imagined that his apartment would look like a typical
bachelor's place, in disarray and helpless abandon, but was pleased
to see that Fernando's home was as neat and clean as her own. She
gazed at the scrimshaws, seashells and brass figures, and the plants
hanging from metal hooks out on the fire escape. He got up and
placed a record album on the turntable. As it spun, a woman with a
voice filled with passion sang a love song which thrilled Amanda.
She too had that record, she told him. He had borrowed it for this
occasion. Relaxed, a bit groggy and feeling free for the first time

in years, she fell into his arms when he pulled her gently by the hand to the center of the room so they could dance slow.

Pressed against each other, she felt the same sensation that drew her to him when they had first met. Gone was the fear that he might harm her, tear her apart, sink her lifeless form into the deepest lake, never to be found. The wind pushed the door closer to its frame and he made a gesture to open it up again, but she asked him not to. Still, she arched her belly back when she felt his thick hardness pressing against the moist warmth between her legs. Lost in an embrace that drew her in again, Fuentes placed his lips against hers and buried his tongue deep into her hungry lips, gently drawing them in and out; she drew his tongue in with motions of her own. The quiet room, the dimness of the place and a sudden surge of uncontrolled desire in her generated an intense excitement that soon made her return the gentle gyrating motions of the hips he gave her. With a pulsing in her very neck and a burning intensity she felt in her entire body, she followed him as he slowly pulled her by her waist, despite her never-ending reluctance, into the shadowy bedroom.

"Please, please. I can't ... "

"It's okay, it's okay, my love."

Her motions were awkward at first and a tightness in her lovespot hurt her a bit as she adjusted and relaxed her muscles to his unusual thickness. Soon they joined each other in rocking motions that made the bedsprings squeak in a steady rhythm. Faster and faster they rocked until, grasping her round, firm buttocks with his rough hands, they climaxed with such an intensity that it almost brought her to tears. Lonely days, lonely nights brought Amanda Gómez silent tears filled with pain.

Later, as she lay with her head against his chest, she asked him if he loved her.

"Yes," he said.

"And René?"

"Him, too."

TEN

In the Bronx, René trudged along 138th Street near Brooke Avenue in search of the Friendly Bar and Grill. Disconsolate, he walked slowly, almost dragging his sneakered feet, as if they contained lead slots. Still thinking about Fuentes, he felt a sudden urge to tear the package apart or hurl it into the nearest trash can. As far as he knew, it might have contained a bomb set to go off when René was far away from 113. He shook it, but heard nothing. He placed it by his ear and then nose. Still no sound or smell. If it contained perfume, it was definitely for a whore, someone at the bar. Like someone trapped in a corner, René thought of killing his enemy to be rid of him once for all. He imagined himself with a gun in his hand, standing over Fernando Fuentes as the sailor slept quietly in his bed. He awakens him with a kick in the ribs and calls him a slimy rat, liar, louse, loaded scumbag, motherfucker. He then commands Fuentes to crawl and beg for mercy, then mercilessly fills him with enough lead to sink him deep into the Atlantic, the same way James Cagney did to punks who double-crossed him.

A large crowd of ticket-holders waited in line in front of the Teatro Puerto Rico. René stopped and stood in front of a life-size cardboard photo of Ramito near the entrance. The Puerto Rican folk singer wore a *pava*, a straw hat with sheered brim symbolizing his simple country roots, and a loose fitting white cotton shirt and highwater white pants. He strummed a thick guitar, while looking up at the sky and standing barefooted on naked soil. René cursed the fools about to pay cash to see and hear this simpleton who probably couldn't write his own name. Yet, the old guy was famous, perhaps rich, adored, envied, imitated and free from the clutches of a merciless hound. René felt miserable and cursed anyone who walked by smiling or laughing. Dazed, he passed by several old delicatessens, barber shops with twirling red and white signs, candy stores where kids his own age laughed, danced, and screamed at each other in fun as the Drifters sang "There Goes My Baby." He passed several *cuchifritos* stands, *bodegas*, shoe shops, boys selling coconut ice cream and snowcones, newsboys screaming out the latest headline and several packed chophouses. He was accosted by several prostitutes and dope peddlers. So muddled were his thoughts that he by-passed his destination.

He noticed his mistake when he looked up and saw the smiling face of John Wayne in a buckskin suit and coonskin cap swinging a long musket at a group of Mexican soldiers at the battle of the Alamo. It was a large blowup display in front of the Casino Theater. René smiled back at the Duke and remembered the many times he'd cheered for him in movie houses and on television. Then he shifted his eyes to the uniformed Mexicans. He stared at their dark menacing faces for a while, part of him wanting to shoot at them, as Davy Crockett and Jim Bowie were doing, and part of him wanting to cheer the Mexicans on. René continued his walk, turned a corner, found the Friendly Bar and Grill and entered.

Inside the bar a deafening blare of trumpets, trombones, congas, timbales and maracas flowed from several large speakers in each corner of the place. They were connected to a jukebox with flashing rainbow lights. Assaulted by the deafening sound, René looked around the dark place. Except for two tipsy barflies that flirted with a busty, guitar-shapped barmaid, the place was nearly empty. She had the kind of face that reminded him of a mannequin: cold, smooth, stiff lips painted deep red, brown eyes peering through black eye lashes. When she saw René, she quickly walked up to him.

"You can't be here, kid. The police won't like it if I give you a drink or something," she said from behind the bar.

"I don't want nothing from you. This here is from Meduso." She stared at the box, then looked over his shoulders and out to the street.

"Wait here," she said sternly, wiggled away and passed through a door between two facing restrooms at the end of the bar. When she returned, she was followed by a young man, about René's age, dressed in a sleek blue suit tailor-made to fit his long, lanky figure. He too looked at the door and window, then signaled René with a snap of his fingers, to follow him back into the room.

The room was an office cluttered with boxes, television sets and radios, tables with rum and brandy bottles. The walls were covered by dark brown wallpaper with thin white stripes that streamed from ceiling to floor. Many framed eight-by-ten pictures of athletes, such as Mickey Mantle, Yogi Berra and Floyd Patterson, and two or three framed portraits of past owners of the Friendly Bar and Grill hung from all four walls. A stale smell of dust, beer and tobacco in the room made René a bit nauseous.

"I'm Cindro Silvera; Silver to you. Who sent you?" the stranger said with a swift dance-like turn of his body.

"I told da lady."

"Never mind that shit; I'm asking you now. Forget the broad. Who sent you?" Silvera demanded with clenched fists and tight jaw as he sat down behind a large wooden desk in the middle of the room. He pulled out a small manila envelope and rolling tobacco paper from a drawer and rolled a marijuana joint. Tall and thin, Silvera seemed lost in his suit. He was so cadaverous looking, with pale sunken cheeks and dark deadly eyes, that René, not knowing what to make of him, looked around for something to hurl at him when Silvera got up suddenly and stood in front of him. A head taller than René, he was stoop shouldered, with a caved-in chest. He stood eye to eye with the long-limbed René Gómez, courier. He eyed René with cold suspicion for a long silent moment without saying anything. Silvera's head was long and narrow, adorned with a crop of long shiny black hair combed and neatly parted to the sides.

"Meduso sent me wid dis stuff."

"Nando?"

"I guess."

"Da marine, right?"

"Yeah."

"Okay, just wanna make sure you ain't no cop pigeon. I just spoke to Meduso on the phone. Gimme da box." He took the package and placed it on the desk, ripped the paper off and opened it with trembling bony fingers. He then stuck a fingertip inside and placed it on his tongue. René noticed the white powder on its way to Silvera's face and recognized it. "H," he thought, that horrible white shit that turned people into sleepy, helpless, worthless, zombies. Junkies were everywhere he looked: the streets, roofs, back yards, buildings. Robbing, shooting, maiming, raping, murdering their way into early graves. Satisfied, Cindro Silvera placed the package in a drawer, pulled an envelope from inside his jacket and handed it to René.

"Okay, here. Give this to Meduso and tell 'im that I need more, now. I have people from all over that bug me all day for the good stuff. That guy is really reliable; always comes through." He feinted a half-hearted smile. "I got more clients I can take care of." He spoke with a dry, tired voice which had a loud ring to it, despite his breathless way of speaking.

"I didn't know I was carrying dat shit."

"Now you know. I don't know you and don't give a shit, but Meduso must'a picked you for a good reason. You mus' owe him money or somethin'."

"I owe him money."

"A lot?"

"I don't know."

"How come?"

"It ain't important."

"He's okay, but weird. Besides, what you care? You gettin' paid, right kid?"

He puffed the thin weed rapidly and spoke sluggishly, as if he were running out of breath, trying desperately not to let the smoke escape from his lungs. He sounded like someone who'd just received a kick in the side ribs. It made René want to laugh.

"I ain't no kid."

Silvera looked at René, then handed the joint to him. René hesitated, then puffed several times, inhaled very deeply and handed it back. The smoke burned his lungs, but he held his breath as he'd seen many a street guy do. With Silvera's dark beady eyes staring at him, René didn't know when to let out his breath and only did so when he felt a pulsing in his forehead and his chest on fire. One long exhalation and a quick breath in allowed René to take several drags before he handed the joint back to Silvera. This was René's first smoke.

"You're okay, kid."

"I told you, I ain't no kid."

"You lucky you're Meduso's friend and I'm wearing this boss suit, it's new. Otherwise I'd mop the floor with you."

"Meduso ain't my friend and you kin take off dat hick suit any time you wan'. I ain't afraid of you."

Silvera laughed loud, hard, so hard he let out a long, painful cough.

"What they call you?"

"René."

"René, I ain't got the time to fight you, some other time. You're okay, man. Let me know when you need work. I can use a gutsy guy like you."

"I don't wanna work for you or Meduso."

"Come by an' see me, anyway. Here's the address to my club. Lots a beer and bitches, you'll do okay." He pointed to the door. "See you."

René stuffed the small paper into his jeans pocket and walked out. He walked past the bar, where the barmaid still resisted the overtures of the two Don Juans. She laughed and stooped forward as she poured fresh drinks into their shot glasses, allowing René and the two men a fine view of her deep cleavage. He could smell her heavy perfume as he walked by. A wavy merengue was playing. A small gathering crowd began to fill the Friendly Bar and Grill.

As he headed towards the subway station, he suddenly felt as if every face on the street were turned towards him with menacing glares. He turned around. No one followed him. The street sounds mixed and multiplied until he couldn't distinguish a yell from a honk. Voices echoed, footsteps and traffic noise mingled to form a hellish din straight out of a horror movie. By the time he reached the corner, he felt as if he had crawled ten endless miles. René yelled out when he felt his feet sinking deep into the concrete. He looked down and saw his feet firmly placed on the sidewalk, but with a burning sensation, as if he were stepping bare footed into hot gray clay. René cursed and yelled and swung his fists and legs in every direction until they felt numb. He hoped desperately that somehow he could clear away the nightmare that surrounded him. People stared at him, cursed him, condemned him to the infernal closet which María Cristina had trapped him into because he had sinned against all heaven. Damned, followed and hunted, he wobbled along, never reaching the subway station. It seemed a hundred miles away. Frightened, not knowing which way to head, he felt panic overwhelm him when he realized that he had lost all control of himself.

Though Silvera was far away from him, René felt his ugly face grinning at him and his bony hands pushing him around like a puppet. He turned around again, but no one was there except a few dark shadows that passed him by. Cindro Silvera. That buzzard with those piercing, narrow eyes and shrill voice, made the ravenous Wolfman in the movies seem handsome and kind. Lost somewhere in a block of empty crumbling buildings with hollow windows, René's head began to clear only after a long struggle. He was convinced that Silvera had added a deadly drug to the smoke. He felt so sick, he vomited alongside a rapidly moving stream of ice cold water that gushed out of an open fire hydrant. He washed his face and rinsed his burning dry throat, as he cursed the son-of-a bitch who had almost killed him.

Certain that Cindro Silvera had tried to poison him, René swore that he would beat the shit out of him and straighten his hunchback with a crowbar. He would grab a bottle, chair, anything, and bash in his miserable pea-brain. With a fury he'd never felt before, he turned around and walked back to the Friendly Bar and Grill, but Silver was gone. No sign of him at the bar. He tried the office door. It was locked. René banged and kicked the door several times, but no one answered. He looked around for a lead pipe to bash Silver's head in, but found none. René wanted nothing more than to dump the vulture's body into the swift stream of the East River, where it'd never be found in it's black muddy bottom. He waited an hour, but Silver did not return. Pressed by the barmaid to leave, René did so when she called a burly bouncer who grabbed him by an arm and pushed him out the door. As he descended the subway stairs, René reached inside his pants pocket and pulled out the address Silver had given him. He read it several times, then placed it in his wallet besides his last dollar bill.

Throughout that long afternoon Silas Turnvil had sat on an empty milk crate near the corner of Park and 109th Street trying to sell a box-load of books and magazines. Most of the shoppers here at La Marqueta strolled by with eyes on the lookout for fruits, roots and vegetables and passed by Silas and his display without the slightest interest. He had spread out several dozen books and magazines on the sidewalk and against a wall between two doorways, but it only caught the attention of a few students looking for old classics. Several market vendors, mostly old friends of the silent shamus, stopped by and greeted him. Whenever a pack of rowdy teenagers cruised by, Silas watched them with an intensity and leeriness bordering on hatred. They wouldn't steal a book, but they sure-as-hell might torment him with sneers or try to take away his few bills and coins. Very few customers approached him despite his bargain sale: twenty five cents for paperbacks; one dollar for hard bound-books. Magazines, new or old, went for dimes and quarters. Good condition; read once, perhaps twice. "Books, books. *Libros, libros,*" Silas Turnvil hawked all day. "*Bueno. Barato. Amigos, Don Quijote,* yours for only a dollar, in Spanish or English."

The stream of shoppers thinned out as evening approached. Tired and a bit hoarse from hawking for hours, Silas picked up an old copy of Herman Melville's *Mardi* and thumbed through the thick allegory. Somewhere in the middle he found a large black butterfly with white blotches on it's wings that reminded him of a Rorschach sketch. He imagined that perhaps it had been placed there by a traveler in some outpost far away. Silas loved making up stories as much as he loved reading them.

He remembered his youthful desire to become an author soon after he fell in love with reading. It was only natural. He too wanted to pen the episodes of his own odyssey, his own journey to the center of the Earth, express his own feelings as an invisible man. He yearned to see his name next to those he loved so much up on one of his bookshelves. But he discovered after years of toil, the gift was not there. Or so he thought when he struggled and labored with writing and re-writing for years on end. Indeed, it sometimes seemed to Turnvil that—in Melville's words—creative writing was like wrestling with an angel called

Art. Each manuscript had a breathing, powerful life of it's own which defeated him again and again. Fictive characters remained almost faceless, a heartbeat away from being real enough to be read and understood. He filled reams with tales and unfinished novels which tried to depict the life of a twentieth-century America he found too difficult to really depict or comprehend. Ever changing, ever growing, ever shocking, his native soil and its diverse faces always led him to the middle of a blank page, a dead end where human drama stopped suddenly, as if a great darkness had covered the world. It was almost futile. The vacuum that surrounded him had produced a near surrender of the heart to really know, care, perhaps love people enough to describe them as they really were. This left Silas Turnvil bitter and occasionally envious of those word-smiths whom the Greatest Author had chosen over him. Who am I? he wondered.

Years of peddling, penning long tales and toiling in the streets of East Harlem made him feel like Taji, *Mardi*'s hero: chasing an illusion. It was no chase, really; he'd given up the quest for an ideal life when Elly died. She wrote poetry. He tried selling some of his writings, but they were rejected again and again. Distraught, he buried a pile of manuscripts in a trunk that fateful day when Elly was no more. But his writing, however superfluous in his judgment, was as much a part of him as his eyes and heart. So he removed the black plastic cover from his old Royal typewriter several months after her death and filled his room once again with the sounds of the keyboard. He was almost there, where the souls that populated his future books began to inhale a slight breath of their own. When the words stopped flowing, he hurled a stack of ink-smeared pages against a bare wall. Silas Turnvil was barely able to note a man's features, let alone his illusive thoughts. The author cursed Homer, Jane Austen, Balzac, Hugo, Joyce, Melville, Wells, Zola, even Bram Stoker—anyone who had wrestled with the angel and won. Why not me? he thought.

As he sat this late afternoon in La Marqueta, he suddenly felt the urge to write something, anything. He looked up and around, glimpsed the images surrounding him and wrote these simple words in his journal.

There is no greater cathedral, no holier edifice, no

greater house of knowledge and worship than a public library. If I could live an extra century, it would only be to read, read, write, write until I got it right; before I sleep.

He looked up when a policeman told him to move on. It was getting dark on Park Avenue. A wino had taken several of his books while he sat deep in thought, writing.

"Maybe he'll have better luck with them," Turnvil said as he loaded and pushed his cart away. Taji still hunted and beckoned ... Sailing on.

ELEVEN

A cool breeze brushed its way across 113 two weeks later as Amanda dusted and mopped her home before going out. She had opened the kitchen and living room windows, allowing a cross breeze to carry the pungent smell of Kingpine out to the street. René's unmade bed was empty. As she made up his bed she realized that she had been doing this for several weeks. He seemed invisible. No matter how early she got up, she always found him gone, his pillow sunk in the middle like an empty baseball glove, his bed sheets dangling from the narrow cot like fallen curtains. When he did come home early, he sat quietly eating his plate of rice and beans and fried meat and gazed at the television set as if he were alone. Amanda cursed the wooden box as an intruder and wished she had never paid so much money for a monster which inspired kids to think like Jerry Mahoney—wooden dummies always sound smarter than their creator. Matt Dillon, Brett Maverick and Cheyenne had more control of René than she did. What a dilemma!

He was as swift and silent as a cat, and no matter how much she tried to tie him down with threats, he always managed to make a clean getaway. He was lost for good in the teaming streets of the barrio.

At first she was convinced that he must have found a girlfriend that kept him up all night. A growing man did these things. She examined his clothes and found no smell of perfume, no lipstick stains, no Bobbi Pins stuck anywhere and no pictures or love letters. Perhaps he'd finally found work, she hoped; but he said nothing to that effect nor did he give her any money. The worst fear for a parent, especially a single parent, was that he might be hooked on drugs. Heroin, marijuana and cocaine were everywhere on the streets of East Harlem. Junkies were as common in the barrio as street fights, greedy landlords and shots in the middle of the night.

Amanda tried several times to stay up until René came home, but sleep overcame her, and she always dozed off before he sneaked in through the window or stealthily through the front door to avoid her harangues. She decided to lock him up somewhere, confine him to the house, until he changed his cruel ways.

René remained tight lipped. When she confronted him one day, all he said was that he was busy trying to earn money by gardening and peddling books with old man Silas. Though it was true that he spent more and more time with Turnvil, René's only payment were books he read and kept and many heartfelt thanks. No one buys books at three o'clock in the morning, she argued. She would have approached Turnvil, but the old man was always unfriendly and mean-looking enough to scare a bulldog away. Amanda tried to stop René by restricting him to the house, but in a building which had but one bathroom per floor, this was difficult. She once waited for him outside the bathroom door for half an hour before she realized that he had escaped through it's narrow window. Finally, Amanda hopelessly threw her hands up in the air and took away his keys. But after a few weeks, she gave up and quit trying to jail him. He always managed to pry open the front window and quietly slip into his bed. Sometimes he climbed up the back wall of the building, holding onto telephone pole cables and a water drain pipe which ran up the house near the kitchen window. The window frame was so caked with old paint, it was impossible to close and it made an easy entry for him.

One day after Amanda finished cleaning, she locked the door of her furnished room and walked upstairs to the second floor. She knocked several times on Luz Castor's door. No response. A loud radio was playing. She knocked louder and kicked the door. She repeated the loud raps several times, trying to drown out the music, until she heard a voice from inside yell out, "Come in!" Amanda felt as if she had entered the Caribe Palace with a full Latin orchestra performing. Luz was speaking—actually yelling—at someone over the telephone. Unable to get a point across, she slammed the receiver into its cradle with a loud crack, lowered the radio slightly, walked Amanda to the couch and sat down next to her.

"Bastard!" Luz yell. She clenched a drink in her tight hand.

She crossed her legs and arms and swung her right foot up and
down as she spoke.

"What, who?"

"Never mind. Want a drink?"

Amanda shook her head.

"You'll never understand," she continued. "Take my advice,
don't trust men. *M'ija*, this afternoon ... "

"Ay, Luz, I don't want to hear another one of your sad stories
about your latest heartbreak. It's always the same. You meet a
guy in a club, *bodega* or subway, then go to bed with him the same
day. No wonder they don't respect you."

"Respect! What does a little fun have to do with respect? Besides, I just don't give it to anybody, like you say. I do have
feelings."

"Yes, but you're too easy ... "

"Hey, what's the matter with you, anyway? You're supposed
to be my friend! You came here to insult me or something?"

"No, of course not, silly woman. You know you're the only
friend I have. What would I do without you in this bad place?
What I mean is this. You say that you hate men because they
deceive you and they use you and always walk out on you. Well,
maybe you make it too easy for them. Try making them almost
beg you for it. Don't chase them, be chased. Don't ever buy a man
drinks, don't ask him to take you home or give him your telephone
number ... unless you really know and desire him. If you don't,
they'll leave you soon after they tire of you. You're one of the
few women I know who thinks that she can act like a man and still
be ... " Amanda searched her thoughts for a word that wouldn't
offend Luz and found: "accepted."

" 'Accepted?' By whom? Society? I don't give a shit about
society any more than it cares about me, especially around here.
I'm not a rabbit to be chased. Besides," Luz added lowering her
voice, "each day I look in the mirror and see more and more lines
coming out of nowhere to torture me. I hate it. It isn't fair. And
the hair beneath Clairol's dye turns as white as my eyes each day.
Why? I'm not even forty! No, thanks, life is too short and full of
misery for a woman. I want to enjoy life while I can, take what I
can take, if it pleases me. As long as men desire me, I'll always

be happy. They use me, I use them. Amanda listen. No one in this world really cares for anyone. We all take without giving unselfishly. Remember that men—all men—don't like old ladies. Jesus!"

"Maybe they like them young because young girls don't complain as much as we do. When they do complain, men don't care, as long as they get what they're after."

"Since when are you an expert on love? You're the one who stays months, years even, without making love."

"I know my place. I'm patient and know the real thing when it comes."

"Have you found it?"

"Maybe. You remember that guy you introduced me to in the Caribe Palace, several weeks ago, Fernando Fuentes? Well, I went out with him last night, and we went to his place. I stayed there real late, you know?" Amanda blushed, then laughed with a gleeful mirth that irritated Luz.

Luz placed her glass down on the coffee table and turned full face to Amanda. A strange wild look, a curious way she had of staring intensely whenever she was confused or angry, vanished and in its place a deadpan stare aimed at Amanda changed her features, until a pallor covered her face and bare arms that chilled and surprised Amanda. Luz got up and poured herself another drink, which burned its way down her already scorched throat. She felt the hot sting and gritted her teeth behind her clenched jaws and tight red lips.

"What's the matter?" Amanda asked. Before Luz could respond, her telephone rang. She picked up the receiver, but it slipped from her hand and banged loudly on the old wooden floor. When she picked it up, she apologized to the person on the other end and added that she had company.

" ... I understand your point," she yelled into the receiver. "I now know more than you think I know. It's okay, okay. I'll talk to you soon, very soon. No, I can't come over. Don't call me again or I'll cut the phone cord. Goodbye!" She hung up with another loud slam. Too taken aback, Amanda didn't dare ask her anything.

The sound of a marching band came in from outside as a large van drove by, blaring John Philip Souza's "Stars and Stripes Forever." It was a voting wagon with big speakers on its roof and several large portraits of Richard Milhous Nixon and Henry Cabot Lodge taped on its sides. Luz dashed to the window. She stuck her upper half outside until Amanda thought she would fall out. Luz, her head filled with rum and an anger that could crush the van and Nixon's pictures in half, yelled at the top of her voice, "Booo! Lousy rich pricks. Get lost, you hypocrites!" Worried, Amanda pulled her back inside. Luz drank another rum and slumped down on the sofa, laughing.

"Amanda, Rockefeller's coming to our block tonight. Imagine! Right here, just a few yards from 113. Why? Come with me, I want to hear what our great governor has to say to us Latinos. He says he likes us and even speaks Spanish. He'll probably say that his buddy Nixon, that man with a smile as warm as a snake's, will tear these buildings down and replace them with projects made of gold bricks: an Eldorado in East Harlem. No more junkies, no more whores, no more hunger and greedy landlords," she sang, then got up and waltzed to the door. "Come on, lets go out."

"What's the other guy's name?" Amanda asked as they walked along the street.

"You mean Kennedy?"

"Yes. I don't know much about what's going on outside of El Barrio, but he looks okay. He's rich and handsome and smart, they say, but he likes the poor."

"I don't like politicians because they all sound alike. 'I promise this ... I promise that,' and when they get elected they forget all about the ignorant poor who placed them in office. But maybe you're right about this Kennedy. Anyway, this has nothing to do with all those jerks that come and go in and out of my life."

"In and out?" Amanda laughed, forgetting Luz's weird behavior just moments ago.

"You know what I mean. Well, not all of them are that way because ... " she stopped short when she suddenly remembered that René was Amanda's son.

"What?"

"No, never mind. I talk too much sometimes. I like to talk about the election because it takes my mind off really important things, like my life."

"You mean like that person on the phone?"

"Yes, but never mind. You don't know men like I do and that's the price I pay for being me. I get to know them so much that I can predict what they're going to say before they open their lying mouths. I can feel on my body what areas they're going to touch before I feel the heat of their hands touch my skin. And I can always hear the final 'farewell, baby, see you very, very soon, I promise' way, way before midnight. Believe me, Amanda, I can twist them like clay when I want to."

"¡Ay, Virgen!" Amanda exclaimed as they disappeared down Fifth Avenue.

Deep within the city's subway system, René rode throughout the five boroughs. Up and down, crisscrossing numbered streets: 5 East, 10 West, 3 South, 9 North. And streets with names: Bay, Bergen, Fulton, Delancy, Corona. Endless avenues: Broadway, Columbus, Fordham Road, Bedford Park, Woodlawn. Always moving, always carrying Fuentes's tightly wrapped packages. Knowing they contained heroine only intensified his fear and growing hatred of the sailor. Meduso, Meduso—he heard the miserable name everywhere. In his own home the name Fernando resounded from the very walls as Amanda repeated his name while doing dishes, cooking or listening to a love song. René hated the man's dress—too slick, too perfect for a rummy sailor and pusher. He hated his wavy hair, his mustache, his tie knotted like a hangman's noose. René wished he could draw that infernal knot with all his might! One quick pull and that would be the end of the sailor; one less bastard in this miserable world. Fernando Fuentes was not a fountain, as his name implied, but a demon who chewed up innocent people and spat them up as dried blood into graveyards. As weeks sped by, René grew more and more nervous. He began to feel pity and sometimes a sharp pain in his gut whenever he saw a junkie sleeping against a trash can, or a girl pushing a baby carriage with knees bent, shoulders hunched, eyelids half closed and dry voiced, too doped up to take a step in any direction. He held on and hoped that someday he could muster the courage to confront Fuentes on even terms and tell him to go fuck himself. Only next time René would be armed and ready. But Fuentes was always armed, tough and clever, ready to kill at a moment's notice.

No, René said, he deserved to be shot from a rooftop or in a dark alley, like a lousy rat. The guys on the block said that there was a special room in every police station where pushers were tortured until they confessed their crimes. He saw the chair, the spotlights aimed at him, the burly men with rolled-up sleeves, thick hairy arms and knuckles the size of walnuts belting him in the gut, punching his skinny back. And always that son-of-a-bitch detective telling him how the guys at The Rock were waitin' to eat his tight little ass. Yeah, dem cats in jail love chicken. Every tall *Americano* René saw wearing a suit and hat was a cop. They always reminded him of those FBI agents in straw hats and wire-rimmed glasses, tracking down John Dillinger in a sweltering Chicago. He'd seen them in countless movies. René's heartbeat quickened whenever he sensed one of these strangers drawing near him.

Once, as he walked along Broadway and 72nd Street, he was approached by a tall, well-built American with a face as pale as a ghost. The man merely said, "Hey kid, come 'ere," and winked at him. René let out as fast as a sprinter at the Olympics. It wasn't until he was a mile or so away that he realized his mistake. "Faggot!" René cursed and delivered the "stuff" to the client, a fancy looking gran dame who told him she once danced in Moscow before the czar. René hated dancing and didn't know what a czar was. He took an envelope she gave him and headed uptown once again.

But this time he had a burning curiosity about the amount inside the envelope and, after waiting a long while for the subway train to arrive, he decided to take a look. The envelope contained a thick wad of twenty dollar bills. His hands shook as he thumbed through the money without taking it out of the envelope. Then the train pulled up half-way through his counting and he stopped, sealed the envelope with his tongue and boarded a car. Free of the pressure of carrying dope and of being followed and caught, he headed uptown on the number five, past the barrio, to Cindro Silvera's place in the Bronx. Fuentes would have to wait for the money. Tempted to run away with the money, René sat back and closed his eyes, while clenching the envelope in his pants pockets. Although the car was filled with people, it would not stop a pickpocket from ripping his pants open with a knife and taking the money right before the other passengers' opened eyes and closed mouths.

René imagined himself somewhere in the fresh hills of Puerto Rico living like a princely don. *Sí, Don René. No, Don René.* Very, very well, *Don René.* You are the master, you are the boss, *gran jefe.* Errol Flynn never had it so good. René Gómez was the real Don Juan. The house of his dreams was built high atop a knoll overlooking the open sea, supported by steel beams bright as the sun, guarded by German Shepherds and surrounded by a high black fence with sharp pikes long enough to impale a dragon. A small waterfall emptied into a pond, down a brook, out to sea. Inside the house, a soft glow of sunshine filtered through the drawn bamboo window shades as he lay across a wide bed framed with a bronze headboard. He watched happily as a naked Luz Castro slowly entered the room with a tall glass of red wine nuzzled between her firm breasts and lay down beside him. Her hair cascaded down her silky shoulders and softly brushed her large, thick-nippled breasts. They seemed more beautiful than ever. She radiated a warmth that filled the dim room and mingled with the heat of the sun. She smiled at him and placed her moist, full red lips on every inch of his body. Luz, Luz, Luz, he whispered. I love you. I love you. Make me come, baby. Kiss me. Hold me. Save me, baby, *mami,* slut.

Kiss me. Curse me, she whispered back, half smiling, half weeping. Fuck me, René. Hit me, René. Love me. René, René, René, her voice echoed in his dream.

The train came to a quick, jerky stop at Simpson Street and he sat up with a start.

Moments later as he walked along the dark streets of the south Bronx, René slowed his quick pace and read each building number carefully because most of the lampposts were blown or smashed and there were big gaps between the tenements. One house read 105, the next 120. He was lost in a mire of old buildings and empty lots. Every street bore a strange name. Every turn that he made led to more dead ends with sleeping winos and aggressive mutts. A man wearing a derby who leaned against a lamppost, cleaning his fingernails with the tip of a stiletto knife, asked René for a handout. René ignored him and quickened his pace. A teenage street walker, thin, painted like a mannequin, approached and propositioned him with a quick upward jerk of her head and a familiar "goin' out?"

"I'm looking for dis place," René told her and showed her the slip of paper.

"That ain't a building, macho."

"It ain't?"

"No. But I can take you dare if you buy me a drink when we get dare."

He agreed and followed her.

"You look like a nice guy, a really nice guy, a pretty nice guy with a nice face, baby. Stay wid me all night long if you wan'. Kiss me, hug me, lick me all you want. Love me and I do da same to you. I promise. I'm good, I'm clean, no clap, a safe girl only for you, *papi*. I promise to be good. Promise to remember you. Honest, *papi*. You're handsome, strong, brave, will you stay wid me tonight?"

They walked a few blocks through several more dark streets so barren that René thought she was leading him into an ambush. The thick wad of bills in his pocket bulged too much. As they walked past an abandoned car he picked up a metal pipe which laid over the hood. The girl noticed and stopped her slow walk.

"Throw it away, man. I ain't gonna do nothin' to you. You're one of us. Watcha scared of? I can't do nothin' to ya. You bigger than me, man. Be cool. Throw that away."

"Just keep walkin'."

She walked ahead, every now and then turning her head and smiling at him. She stopped in front of a store front with its windows painted red. It had a heavy metal door with a speakeasy slot in the middle, and bone white letters on the portal that read, "Arco Nuevo Social Club." From inside came the sounds of people yelling, laughing, coughing and talking above the voice of Chuck Berry as he sang "Roll Over Beethoven" amid a background of drums, base and guitars. The girl pressed a doorbell beneath a glass peephole. A pair of red eyes from inside stared at them for a moment. A heavy-set man with gloved hands opened the door with a heavy thud.

Inside, they walked past a large pool table just three feet from the entrance and sat at the bar. The Arco Nuevo was divided in half. On the entrance side there was the pool table and the bar. A thick wall made of two-by-fours sheeted with slabs of thin wood paneling ran up the middle of the place, ending just four feet from the middle of the bar. Small round tables adorned with plastic clothes and burning glass-encased candles lined the walls; a flashing jukebox, which never rested, filled a deep niche in a wall. The floor was packed with dancers too young for regular clubs. Behind the bar a robust man in his sixties served drinks and answered the phone. Between liquor bottles were dozens of bronze trophies his baseball team, Arco Nuevo, had won in amateur competitions. These he polished with a white cloth as often as possible; some figures had their faces rubbed clean of their gild.

"What can I get you?" he asked René.

"Two beers."

"I wan' somethin' strongah ... "

"Give her a whiskey. A double whiskey," René said wishing to be rid of her.

Within minutes someone took her by the hand and led her away to dance, and they disappeared into the darkness of the small dancing room. Relieved, René quickly found a small empty table near the jukebox at the other end of the room and sat down with his beer.

Here he could scan the crowd without being noticed. They were mostly teenage guys with thin ties, shark skin suits, pointed shoes. Some wore T-shirts and jeans. The girls wore multicolored skirts which hung an inch or two above their knees and hugged them tight around the hips. René wondered how these girls could move around, let alone dance, in such tight-fitting skirts. They reminded him of large upright fish trying to swim up and down. Yet he loved to look at those bouncing round asses, quivering tits, pink lips, frosted hair, Cleopatra eyes. Now the coin-filled jukebox produced the joyful sounds of Machito and his band as if they were there in person. Guitars, *timbales*, horns and maracas filled the Arco Nuevo with a joyful melody which seemed endless to a drunken few, too short for those dancing. The dancers twirled and laughed, following the rapid beat as René sat back and smiled, enjoying the scene. When the next record began, a loud cheer went up and the dance floor turned into a packed rush-hour subway car as Chubby Checker's toy voice sang out, "Come on baby, let's do the Twist!"

The dancers twisted their bodies swaying left and right, their hands clenched, punching away like boxers, their heads wiggling like strung puppets, always smiling, always laughing.

René looked to his side when he felt someone sit down and stare at him.

"Hey, kid. Glad you made it," Silvera said gleefully.

"You're weird, man. Where you come from?"

"Prob'ly Hell, nobody knows ... "

"Listen, shit head, you almost poisoned me a few weeks ago. I only came hear to tell you to step outside."

Silvera laughed and pounded his fists lightly on the table several times. "Man, you got some set of *cojones*. You come all da way up here just for dat shit?"

"You tried to kill me, mudafucka!"

Silvera laughed louder. "You know all I have to do is nod an' all dese guys here'll jump you? Look, I put no weird shit in dat smoke. I smoked da same stuff an' was okay. Ain't you ever smoke?"

"No."

"See, dat's it. You'll get use to it. Da more you smoke da less it screws your brain. One day you'll be able to smoke a whole nickel bag an' feel nothing. Hey look, forget dis shit. I got more important things for you. I told you I can use a slick cat like you." He looked around. "Come on, I want to show you something."

Silvera got up and René followed him to the back of the club. In a corner near the back wall, a small rectangular banister stood above an opened floor door with a narrow wooden staircase which lead to a small basement. A bright light came from downstairs. As René followed Silvera down the stairs he heard the sound of familiar voices.

Some of René's friends from East Harlem were sitting around a table in the middle of the room. A thick cloud of gray and white smoke hovered over them as they talked, drank and ate warm Caribbean food served by a short stocky woman wearing a stained apron. The steam from a large bowl of yellow rice and a long metal tray stacked with beef steaks smothered with onions rose and mixed with the cigarette smoke before being sucked out through a half open window high up a wall close to the ceiling. The glass had been painted black.

"Hey, René what's happenin'?" Dutch asked. He was a friend of René's who lived in the building facing 113.

"Hi. Silver invited me here. Glad to see you guys," René replied as he slapped hands with everyone seated. He sat down, then remembered what Silvera had said about his "boys" and wondered if these fellows, guys René knew, would side with Silvera and attack him. Better keep quiet. "What you guys doin' up here? Da Bronx ain't your turf. It's crummy up here."

"No different than the barrio," someone said.

"We're partying an' doin' somethin' else. Somethin' special," Dutch said.

"What you mean?"

"Remember what I sed a few weeks back about hittin' dat Jewish church in our block?"

"Mean da temple? Sure. I t'ink so," René said thinking back. He had spent so little time with them this summer that he'd nearly forgotten about them and their endless rap sessions. He had lost patience with them and grew to hate sitting around prattling all day long. Money, women, freedom urged him onward. He'd wasted too much precious time already.

"Dare's gotta be lotsa things in dare worth lotsa money," Silvera said, "a real treasure."

René remembered that day, as if it had occurred the year before; so much had happened to him lately he'd lost all track of time. Yesterday seemed so far away. Gold, treasure, booty gleamed in his eyes once again when Dutch and Silvera spoke about Mount Pisgah as if it were a hidden Eldorado. René smiled to himself and remembered that look of happy surprise on the Count of Monte Cristo's face on the cover of a Classics Illustrated comic book: hands dripping with sparkling jewelry, gleaming coins falling from between his clenched fists, a trunk-load of riches that had made a nobleman out of a poor criminal. Then the vision vanished in a puff when the sounds around René brought him back to the Arco Nuevo. These guys were stupid punks who daydreamed more than he did. A rich horde in so poor a place as a synagogue in the middle of a ghetto? No way. Old man Silas certainly didn't look rich. In fact, Silas, though a weird cat, was as much a ragamuffin as any one of them. Still, they were persistent and he listened out of sheer curiosity. It would be great if true. But Silas mustn't be around. No telling what might happen.

"Who's goin' to buy all that Jewish stuff? If we don't get rid of it, we be stuck wid it," René said.

"I will," a deep voice answered. René turned around and saw a man emerging from the shadows of a dark closet toilet. It was Fernando Fuentes, the last person in his thoughts at that moment, in that strange hole in the Bronx. "Nice to see you, René. Surprised to see me here? See kid, I get around." He sat down and signaled the cook for a drink.

"I bin lookin' for you," René said as he handed the envelope to him. Fuentes pulled out his knife, pressed the red button on its handle, which sprang out its sharp blade, and used it as a letter opener. The gang stopped talking and stared at Fuentes' hands as he held the envelope with one hand and thumbed the inch thick bills with the other. He placed them in his suit jacket and addressed René.

"Sure, René. Never mind that for now. What's this about a treasure, Silver?"

"You heard. Me an' dese guys found a rich place to hit. A syna-somethin', you know dat temple in René's block. I once went into a place like that. I was walkin' by an' an old man wid a beard an' black coat came out an' asked me if I would turn on da lights inside for him. I think it was a Jewish holiday an' he wasn't suppose' to work or turn nothin' on—who da fuck knows or cares. Anyway, when I pulled all the light chains in da place, I thought I was in Fort Knox: lotsa fancy gold and silver things. I was only twelve, but I remember. I ain't lying. What you think, Meduso?"

"I believe you because I know it's true," Fuentes said, intrigued by the story. Like a prospector searching in the wilderness, he followed the vision and magnified it in his own words until it seemed as real to the boys as the ring of a cash register; one key pressed, out sprang money.

"If it's real and we take it, why should we give it to you?" René asked.

"It isn't real treasure, kid. That only happens in movies. It's just a lot of valuable things of no use to you. But if you get it for me, I'll pay you half of what I get when I sell the stuff at the docks. Maybe a few hundred bucks apiece for each of you. Not bad for one day. If you get it, I'll give you other jobs. That stuff ain't worth much to you the way it is."

"If we get caught? ... " René asked. "I don't wanna go to jail."

"You won't."

"How you know?" Dutch asked.

"I'll pull the job with you," Fuentes promised.

"If we get caught with the stuff?" someone asked.

"You won't."

"How you know?"

"Look, you guys ask more questions than a cop. I tell you there's gold in there ... "

"They say them Jews is rich ... "

"They say them Jews are poor ... "

"There's gold and silver inside ... "

"I say we go!"

"Yeah!"

"Boys. I'll tell you a little secret. All that stuff will never be found because it's going to be melted."

"Melted?" René cried out.

"Yeah. Right down to the last once. Not a trace of it will remain as it is now. So they won't pin a fucken thing on you ... or me."

Silence. They all stared at one another without saying anything for almost a full minute. Then they burst into a wild uproar that drowned the music above their heads. "We go in two days, okay?"'

Before they could say anything else, a loud bang, as if someone were breaking down a door upstairs, made them snap up and run to the bottom of the stairs.

"Oh shit! The cops!" Silvera yelled as he jumped up and smashed the bare bulb that lit the room.

Fuentes took a metal folding chair, broke the small window, them climbed out and ran outside and disappeared into the back yard. René followed him, slipped out the window, ran over mounds of rubble, stumbled across beams and boxes and emerged on a dark street corner, just two blocks away. Fuentes had vanished. He looked back and saw several police cars and a paddy-wagon being loaded with some of the people that were at the club. A drug bust, he thought. René hoped that Fuentes and Silvera were among those caught. But he didn't see them anywhere. He walked out to the street slowly, casually, staying close to a wall of buildings, like someone out for a nightly stroll. When he got to the Madison Avenue bridge, he ran across it and continued his trek down Lexington until he reached 113.

Out of breath and as frightened as a hunted animal, he climbed the front steps of the building, reached out and tried to pull the window open, but found it locked. A police patrol car siren screamed out from the corner of Park. René looked to his left nearly feeling heavy hands on his arms, handcuffs around his wrists. Can't be, can't be, he said, and ran to the back of the building. Beneath his window he pulled himself up the drain pipe, but his slippery hands couldn't hold a firm grip and he fell down after a four foot climb. He dried his hands on his pants and ascended once more until he reached his open kitchen window. Except for some flickering shadows that came from María Cristina's window, the yard was very dark. He entered quietly, passed his sleeping mother and slipped into his cot. Within minutes he was tossing and kicking his legs as if he were still being chased.

TWELVE

Very soon after the night of her mystic vision, María Cristina Cruz had another dazzling revelation. From then on, her mission was rekindled with new energy: she would spread the Good News to the bitter end and save as many souls as St. Paul himself. Until now she had restricted her mission to vigilant prayers and church volunteer work. She felt happy singing in the choir and helping victims of poverty find food and shelter. She started visiting all her old friends systematically to tell them at length about the coming of the new kingdom. Nineteen Sixty was the year, she told them. Look around, see for yourselves ... This took her to all parts of the city.

She found Coney Island filled with lewd, vulgar loud-mouths who got drunk and had sex beneath sheets on the open beach or under the boardwalk. The Bronx, with its many bars, honky-tonks and street hoods, proved a threat to her safety, but she did not care—God always protects the good. And Times Square shocked and horrified her. It was the most hellish street on Earth: hookers, pushers, petty thieves on every corner. The police did little to chase them away. In any case, she handed out flyers, preached the gospel, quoted its golden words in Spanish and in English.

Most people smiled or ignored her in silence as they hurried by. Others stared and listened, nodding their heads in agreement. Some gazed through half-closed eyes, too tired or stoned to really care. And a bold few asked her questions concerning her revelation. "How do you know these things?" "Why were you chosen?" "Why should He love you more than me?" "Children are innocent. They should never never suffer." "God created this world as a gift to us." "Life itself is a gift." "I've done nothing wrong to repent of."

María Cristina often showed her audiences a printed chart depicting Heaven and Earth. Some saved souls flew freely above the clouds wearing white robes, spreading dove white wings, while the condemned suffered the torments of Hell in the furnace of the nether world. "For many are called, but few are chosen ... The Time is near," she warned. Two or three individuals promised her that they would repent soon and join her crusade against evil—as soon as they sobered up—for the glory of God and the defeat of Satan. But they were mainly outcasts, strangers and vagabonds with nothing but their rags and grime. To María Cristina, they were the ones that needed the most salvation. Hadn't the Lord proved that? Some were skeptics who only wanted to play with the old, ranting woman. She preached in La Marqueta, on subway cars, even on streets where she stood alone, hoping someone passing by would stop and listen. María Cristina also sang hymns and played a tambourine, warning between songs of a day of reckoning.

One warm evening, shortly before midnight, she arrived home exhausted. She felt hungry and her throat was sore; her lower back, legs and feet burned with a pulsing sensation. With barely enough strength to secure her door locks, she turned to her right, bent her knees, touched the edge of her mattress and threw herself across the bed in total darkness.

In a semi-conscious state, she sat up when she thought she heard footsteps coming from the kitchenette. She sat up and faced her darkened altarpiece, rested her aching head against the wall. She closed her eyes tight for a moment, then opened instantly when she thought she heard the sound again. A strange glow began to appear near her altar. Thinking she had left a candle burning, she made a faint move to get up and snuff out the candle, but held back when she saw it wasn't a flickering wick that glowed. Though she hadn't drank liquor since she'd "found the Lord," she felt light-headed, in a groggy stupor, not knowing whether she was asleep or awake. She adjusted her eyes as the gray glow broadened, lengthened and took the form of a man.

"Jorge!" she whispered. It looked at the old woman and nodded.

Stern, unsmiling, unlike his living self, wearing the same blue suit and green tie he'd worn in his coffin, the figure had a look of sadness on it's face which puzzled her. María Cristina was not afraid. She pulled a rosary from beneath her pillow and held it between her bony fingers. She pulled the cord with her left hand, the small round black beads running smoothly between her right thumb and index finger like a tiny train. She had seen and spoken to many of her ancestors since childhood and even sighted lost souls who had wandered across her path one time or another, but this was the first time that she had seen Jorge. María Cristina had waited for her son since the day he'd been buried in Saint Raymond cemetery in the Bronx. There was so much she wanted to know.

"*Hola, madre,*" it said in a double voice which echoed. The vision had split itself and was now two identical figures, speaking simultaneously.

"What do you want from me, son?"

Silence.

"Are you hungry?" María Cristina asked.

"Never," they said.

"Are you cold?"

"Impossible."

"You killed yourself and left me alone. Will They let you rest. Will He forgive you?"

"Perhaps. I must wander a while, but tonight I was given a short time to visit you. You are the lucky one, though mortal and soon to be like me. You can still breath precious air, sing, be warm by the sun." Jorge spoke in a slow, tired monotone voice. Yet, he had regained his youthful, handsome features. His long, thin face was taut, smooth, tamarind-hued. He was tall and wore a thin mustache and black beret, as he appeared in the photograph on the wall behind him.

"Soon?" Her eyes opened wide and rested on one figure, then the other. "To be like you?"

"Yes, but I cannot tell."

"What should I do? I know the way. I saw the Sign. I do as He commands, but no one listens, few pay heed. Why is it so difficult?"

"Men are blind and say they see, but the only thing they see is themselves: on earth, in heaven, in dreams, in the sea, the stars, the clouds, black space, in hell, in their hearts, minds, everywhere and everything."

"What should I do?"

"Take The Word with you everywhere. Help others. He will forgive you your sins and wrap you in a white cloud of glory."

"But ... "

"Remember to remember to remember ... " the voice faded along with the vision.

"Jorge!" María Cristina cried out, "Come back, son. I need to know. I need to know, I need ... " With a start she got up, fully awake and turned on the ceiling light. Dripping in perspiration and shaking, she drank a glass of cold water from the refrigerator as she came to her full senses, like someone awakening from a long, restless dream.

Loud bangs of hammer blows and a crackling buzz sent chills down René's spine and awakened him abruptly one morning. It was shortly before noon. He had come in from the streets shortly after four in the morning and had overslept. Drenched in perspiration, he felt as if he had slept in a warm pond somewhere in the wilds. Amanda moved around quietly doing little chores, every now and then throwing a piercing glance at René, as if she'd just bagged a sleeping tiger who might spring up and whisk away. René looked at her with droopy eyelids, sat up on the side of his cot and faced the window. He pulled up the dark-green plastic shade that his mother had bought at Woolworth's and blinked as a ray of sunlight hit his sleepy face and filled the room with a blinding summer brightness. Dust particles danced in the sunlight and settled all around him. He opened the window and poked his head outside. The noise was coming from the open yard on the left side of 113 as carpenters assembled a makeshift wooden stage in the center of the lot, ten feet from the edge of the concrete curb. The carpenters were followed by a group of young men and women. They were mostly clean-cut Joe College types who gave the impression to the block folks of having come straight from a farm in Kansas or who were members of the Mormon Tabernacle Choir moonlighting for the GOP in the city of sin and democrats. The young men sported blond crew-cuts and wore short-sleeved check-

ered shirts and baggy trousers. Their girlfriends were thin, mostly
sandy-haired girls in their late teens, dressed in pleated white or
blue skirts adorned with flowers and red stripes, and brown penny
loafers. They handed out thousands of campaign flyers to the unin-
terested Harlemites. The discarded papers were all over the lot, on
the street and on Lexington and Park Avenues. White chicks, René
thought, with smooth white necks and tits, vanilla ice cream with
cherry. They gave him the impression that they were all named
Betsy. The guys: Hank or Bud, Latter Day Saints. These volunteers stapled red, white and blue banners and portraits of Richard
Nixon and Henry Cabot Lodge on the front and sides of the stage.
Made of foot-wide plywood planks, it formed a six-foot square
bordered by a railing of two-by-fours which opened to the back of
the lot and lead to a couple of steps just two feet above brown and
black soil. Loudspeakers were added to the front corners of the
stage and, immediately after being hooked up, they pored forth
a salvo of campaign songs in English and Spanish, followed by
recordings of highlights from classic Republican speeches which
exalted the virtuous the GOP and Vice President Nixon. A little spice was added when several of Tito Puente's records were
played.

"René, come inside. You'll fall if you look out any further."
Amanda handed him a cup of coffee and a saucer of Ritz crackers.
He took it and set it down on the window ledge. A short while
later, when he had washed and dressed, he sat down once again to
finish his coffee.

Amanda sang Spanish melodies as she straightened up the stu-
dio apartment. She asked him the same questions she had asked
him a thousand times before. His answers were always short and
vague. She gave up when he diverted the talk to her.

"You never used to sing so much, Mom. You okay?"

"Remember when you was a little boy an' I used to ask you
why people sing an' you couldn't answer? Den I said dat people
sing because dey're happy? I've never ever seen anyone cry and
sing at the same time. Have you?"

"I have."

"When?"

"One night when I was thirteen, I climbed up the stairs of Saint

Cecilia's Church on a Good Friday and saw this cat singin' and cryin' his red eyes out as he sang somethin' like 'Behold the Clam of God.'"

"I'll never understand you kids—you keep changing words around!" she cried. "Cat! You mean, man. An' it ain't clam, but lamb. Damn dis lousy barrio an' what it does to kids. When I was a *señorita* in Puerto Rico, being a teenager was no big deal. In fact, it was somethin' we wanted to get over with fast so we could be adults, real people. Here, people ain't people but "cool cats," money ain't money but "bread," a dance is a "jump"—is dat what you do in a party, jump all night like silly bunnies?"

"Keep singin', Mom."

"Are you telling me to shut up?" Amanda yelled.

"No. It's just dat you're different dan before. I never seen you singin' so much an' be so happy all da time."

René stared at her for a long while. He had forgotten how young and pretty his mother was and how proud he had felt as a little boy whenever someone complimented her on her beauty or mistook them for brother and sister. Near her, on the mantelpiece, was a picture of her when she was about seventeen. He looked at the picture and was surprised by the simple face and the wholesomeness of the pretty girl dressed in the style of the 40's. Young Amanda had that kind of fresh innocence of a Judy Garland, who never said anything harsher than "gosh" and spoke with a sad cry in her voice because she was lost in a hostile world. But now there was a hardness and impenetrable look that was slowly edging its way across her face and settling around her eyes, adding a tinge of permanent sadness to an otherwise perfect face.

"I'm happy, yes. Happier dan ever. Except when I think of you an' da many headaches you give me. Where you go all da time? Why're you so quiet all of a sudden? Did I do somethin' wrong?" she asked. Before he could reply, she continued. "Why you want to be away all da time? Dis house ain't no jail, but your home. You don't eat here, you don't stay long, you don't even bath here. You only sneak in an' out through da window when I'm sleeping. I leave it open sometimes because I don't want to suffocate in dis damn heat. Comes winter an' you goin' to have to sleep in da basement wid da cats and rats if you keep dis shit up! Where do you eat? Where do you go? I'll ask you a million times 'til I get an answer, so don't worry."

René could feel the dragonheat from her red lips hit his face. He looked down at the tall coffee mug between his palms as he rolled it like a ball of brown clay. The mug had an inch or so of cold brew in its bottom that reminded René of a well. Perhaps it had a deep, dark shaft into which he could descend to its very depths and disappear into a tunnel and cave where no one would find him. He had seen something like that in a movie. There he would rule over creatures smaller than himself, creatures he could step upon if he wished and not be bothered by them again. King René, the mighty ruler of a kingdom. Yet he also remembered that the cave in the movie was ruled by a hairy brute who led a tribe of imps that prayed upon helpless people. That brutish ruler was someone like Fernando Fuentes.

"I eat anywhere, Nedick's, Horn and Hardart's, an' I go on errands for Fuentes."

"Errands?" she asked, surprised.

"Yeah. Like he gives me stuff for me to deliver all over da city. Dat's why I'm never home. I'm always busy ... " he answered still fixed on the mug in his hands.

"Stuff?"

"Plants, herbs, souvenirs ... "

"Dat's nice. He's so good. He speaks about you all da time an' says how good you are, how he can teach you many thing's an' how he feels like a father for you. You're a good, smart kid, he says. A lot he knows! If he could only live here wid us, he'd soon see how bad you are sometimes, *m'ijo.* Anyway, das nice of 'im to feel dat way. Fernando is a good man dat wan's to take care of me an' you."

"No, he ain't. I'll take care of us. We don't need no greasy sailor with a pimp mustache here ... "

"Stop it or I'll break your mouth! You ain't too big for me to smack dat fresh mouth of yours. He don't look like no pimp. He's a *caballero* wid a proud mustache, somethin' you'll never be if you keep dis shit up," she yelled with arms akimbo and angry, pouting lips. She wore a white dress with short sleeves that reached her ankles just inches away from her small sandled feet. They were standing in the middle of the room.

"Besides, if you don't like him why you work for 'im?"

"I need the bread."

That evening, René came home early after spending the day shopping in La Marqueta for a shirt and a new pair of sneakers. Fuentes had given him several dollars as an advance for what he called the "temple job." More a rape than a job, René thought, an' I'm a rapist. But, René was too deeply involved with Fuentes not do as Fuentes ordered. René still felt the sting of the sailor's knife at his throat. Besides, the prospect of riches cheered him and, for the first time this summer, he began to see things in a new light. A surge of happiness overwhelmed him whenever he envisioned himself possessing lots of money, fine clothes, gorgeous girls. True, he still hated the sailor, but at the same time Fuentes had an odd charm that drew people to him. Like someone caught in a thick net, René had quit struggling and surrendered. He couldn't tell whether it was Fuentes's words, his dark forceful ways, or his sinister charm that made him almost impossible to shake off.

One day, Fuentes told him to keep fifty dollars. The following week he increased it to one hundred. A bit more later on. René had paid his debt. The miserable junk he'd stolen from Fuentes was finally paid for. The knife at his throat was withdrawn, the prick and sting forgotten, the mental image of his own grave just another hole in the ground. With each succeeding week, the bundle in the envelopes grew larger and his share in it increased with each run. Yes, he still hated the merchant marine, but the hatred turned into a sometimes brooding resentment that made René feel like a factory worker who curses his boss when his back is turned.

René bought shirts, pants, hot-dogs galore, snow cones with rainbows of syrup. He went to the Eagle Theater on Third, the RKO and Loew's Orpheum on 86th Street and a dozen others on Times Square. In Coney Island he rode the Tornado roller-coaster, thrilled at the Parachute Jump, rode the Steeplechase horses again and again. As he returned home, he wished that he had lived to see Coney's Luna Park and Dreamland, places he'd seen pictured in one of Silas Turnvil's books. He bought flowers and wine for Luz Castro, whose door and arms were always open to him. In bed she always cried out his name, bit his ears, dried his smooth body with a soft, sweet-smelling towel. One night he kissed and licked her smooth tan feet until she giggled in ecstasy because she had done that to him. Then she rolled him over and straddled him. All these riches without having to work his ass off pumping gas or soda, or delivering groceries or dry-cleaning along Park and Madison, below 96th Street. He stopped shining the shoes of those fuddyduddies on 86th Street who rested their big feet on his shoe box because they felt sorry for him or had no one else to talk to. René bought a pair of black loafers for special occasions and had the young shine boys of Lexington shine them until they gleamed like a black limousine. Soon they'd have to call him Mister Gómez.

René wanted desperately to take his mother away from East Harlem, and perhaps build two houses near that pond with the beautiful waterfall which once belonged to the Gómez family in Puerto Rico. One house for mother, one house for himself and the beautiful girl of his dreams. That simple.

But too many were the days when he'd walk past the Ortiz Funeral parlor and peer through its meshed side window to see kids his own age laying stiff, hands folded on their flat laps, with a rosary resting on them. The well attired boys were powdered, had lips drawn back stiff, eyes moist; they were eternally asleep in a heroine high impossible to awaken from. René Gómez, seventeen, lover, dreamer, realized one day that he had helped place those people in that awful place. It was better not to think.

One afternoon, René had lain in bed staring at the ceiling and dozing off for brief spells, despite the bright sunlight. When evening arrived, he turned a lamp on and laid down again. Whenever he looked up, he squinted and searched among the chips and cracks, islands, streams, sailboats and schooners, halyards and rusty anchors in search of escape, but he saw nothing except the stark cruel face of reality about to slap him hard across his puzzled face. What romance lays in a broken ceiling? Nothing seemed real anymore.

The music outside had grown louder and the political speeches more numerous. René heard loud boos, shouts and applause. Since noon, the loud speakers had not rested. Each *mambo, merengue, bolero, güaracha* had been followed by a campaign song or march which echoed between Temple Mount Pisgah, 113, the Parish of

Saint Cecilia and the wall of gray buildings across the street: 112, 114, 116 and the granite wall of the railroad on Park. Men, women and children snapped their fingers, shouted, danced in the middle of the street and screamed whenever they heard Chubby Checker, the Palmieri brothers or the Drifters singing their hearts out to them. Above the music and shouts, the loud piercing sound of police car sirens filled the block. René walked the half dozen yards that separated 113 from the campaign stage. He stood directly in front of the platform with arms folded. A young man, about René's age, sat near a wooden box with many wires connected to a record player. He was feeding it a stack of 45 RPM records one at a time from a pile that lay between his bony legs on the platform floor.

Behind a podium at center stage, the Governor of New York State, Nelson A. Rockefeller, stood waving at the crowd. He wore a dark suit and a pair of black horn-rimmed glasses that reflected the spotlights on the front ends of the stage. Rockefeller smiled broadly as he waved and tried to calm some of hecklers in the crowd.

"*¡Amigos!*" he said in Spanish, "*Muy buenas tardes.* If you look around you will see nothing but decay. Well, we could let it get worst by electing a Democrat to the White House." The crowd cheered. "Or, we could continue to progress by helping the poor in the tradition of the Republican Party." The governor's voice was drowned by laughter and jeers and a chorus of "We want Kennedy! We want Kennedy! We want Kennedy!" Rockefeller smiled broadly until his eyes resembled long slits with crow's feet at their ends. René was puzzled. As little as he knew about politics and anything outside East Harlem, he could not help but ask himself, How could a rich man who'd made so many promises—especially to the Latino poor of this barrio—and done so little 'till now, be trusted? René, too, raised his voice and shouted with his people.

"They say that every tree has roots which are impossible to remove from the soil," Rockefeller continued. "Well, my friends and fellow Americans—for so you are—I assure you that your roots in El Barrio will be here forever. If you want to grow, I urge you to elect Richard Nixon to the presidency."

René walked slowly through the crowd. Amanda was there.

So was Luz. His mother stared blankly; Luz grew angrier with each word the Governor uttered, and she folded her lips to prevent herself from screaming out another curse. She had grown hoarse from cursing and yelling all day long.

Several men in the crowd, tired of shouting and booing, lost their patience with the governor and hurled a hail of stones and rubble in the direction of the stage, knocking down a loud speaker, smearing Nixon's pictures with ketchup and eggs. Undaunted, always smiling, the governor continued speaking while a squad of policemen started arresting some of the ruffians. There were more shouts, curses, catcalls, "We want Kennedy! We want Kennedy!" and several tomatoes were thrown at the governor. At the end of his speech, Rockefeller yelled out with a cheerful voice and smile, *"¡Qué Viva Puerto Rico!"* A few people applauded and whistled and received winks and hand waves from the grateful official. He was safely escorted back to his limousine where he sat in the back seat and waved at the crowd from behind his closed window. The car departed, turned the corner and headed down Lexington. When a volley of stones was hurled at the car, another troop of police officers dove into the crowd and picked out several more men and boys, clubbed them with their night sticks and pushed them into a paddy wagon.

René walked away from all this after seeing his mother and Luz to the safety of the steps of 113. He had seen riots only in movies. Frightened, excited and tempted to hurl a stone, for some unknown reason he remained passive because he didn't understand what the fuss was all about. Nor did he really care. People were always bitching about one thing or another in the barrio. Who really cared? He was on his way to meet Fuentes, Cindro Silvera and the others, hoping that one day he too could drive away from 103rd Street in a black limousine, waving back at his adoring people. Only then there would be no stones for René Gómez to receive or throw.

THIRTEEN

Shortly before midnight that same evening, 103rd Street was as silent as the day had been noisy. Gone were the shouts and jeers, gone were the young volunteers. The loud speakers had been carried away to another block, borough, city, state. There was nothing left of the campaigners but the empty stage and the heaps of rubble surrounding it. The electric wires were gone and the billboards torn down. With exception of a trio of homeless tramps who lay sleeping beneath the wooden stage, the block was silent, almost deserted. Every now and then a diesel powered train sped by leaving a thick cloud of smoke and a series of echoing sounds. It would vibrate against the old buildings for a short while before fading into the night.

René and his friends gathered one by one under a railroad underpass which crossed his block. They smashed several small glass-encased light bulbs that lit the underpass and sat down on the hard ground. Except for a few vehicles which sped by throwing brief flashes of light at each entrance, the tunnel was very dark. The boys squatted and spoke in low tones as they waited for Fernando Fuentes.

René remembered the night he had broken into the sailor's home. He had felt very nervous and apprehensive that night. He still felt cold chills whenever he recalled how he'd mistaken that stuffed duffel bag beneath Fuentes' bed for a corpse. He remembered how every sound that came from outside had terrified him, stopped him dead in his tracks. Now, in the midst of a gang, he felt as if he were about to enter the First National Bank and walk away loaded. There was a bit of Jesse James in René Gómez; he wasn't about to let his legendary hero down. This was certain. It was nearly two a.m. and not a single police officer was in sight. There would be no one in Mount Pisgah at this hour; no rabbis, crowds, no well-dressed old men who wore skull-caps in or out of the temple, no cantors or delivery boys, no shamas. Mister Turnvil was probably resting his tired old body in his narrow cot between books, records, papers, carving knives, silver and gold powder. He'd continue to stare at the picture on the wall. "Ely, Ely," René had once heard him whisper in the garden when Silas thought he was alone.

"You know, Silver," René said, staring into the darkness surrounding them, "you're a boss dresser an' make pretty good bread sellin' junk and shit. Why you want dat stuff inside da temple?"

"Same as you, kid: money. I ain't got as much as you think, so I want more. Can't never have enough. Nobody can. Ever noticed that gangsters are rich an' famous? An' when dey die, books are written about dem, an' songs tellin' how brave dey was, an' always dey make movies about dem? Me an' you guys is nothin'. We live an' die an' no one cares or remembers. I bet dare's more movies about Al Capone dan about Washington. But I hear dey both died of syphilis. Anyway, da only difference between us an' dem real gangsters is dat dey never get caught. An' if dey do, dey always have a bunch of mouth-pieces to get dem outta jail. Who cares for me an' you guys? Nobody, dat's who."

"You ever bin busted?"

"Yeah. Got my ass kicked lotsa times in da station house an' in jail. Doze suckus won't be happy 'til dey fry my ass in da 'lectric chair. Ever seen a rich man get da hot seat? No! Never! An' you never will. I bet a rich big shot scientist invented da fucken hot seat, but never sat on it himself, phoney prick. It ain't fare, I tell ya." They all laughed. Their voices echoed in the tunnel. "I dig havin' fine threads, a nice pad an' a chick dat turns heads. Only one thin' I need to get dem things: good money. An' wit' dat, maybe people'll give me respect."

"Will we find what Fuentes says?" someone asked.

"Yeah," Silver answered. "He's okay."

"What'll we find?"

"Gold."

"Silver."

"Jewels."

"Money."

"Diamonds."

"Books made of ivory."

A gleeful mirth overtook them and they laughed aloud. Each of the boys told what they would do with the money. Within a few minutes they had bought houses on sandy Caribbean islands, fancy cars, beer, smoke, great food and they had the finest chicks on Earth.

"When I was ten," René said," I used to shine shoes wid guys from around here on 86th Street. Some ole men also shined shoes, but dey tipped da cops off an' had me chased away. I swore dat someday—when I grow to be a bigshot—doze dumb cops would come to me for tips. Den da only tip dey'd get would come from my shoe or knife! Bein' rich, I'd escape an' live in da jungles of P.R. wit' my ole lady." He spoke in a low voice that was amplified by the granite wall of the underpass.

"They got jungles in P.R.?" someone asked.

"Maybe, maybe not. If dey ain't any, I'll grow one." They laughed aloud. "I heard someone say dat nothin's impossible. I can do what I want ... " René hesitated when he saw a man enter the passageway from the east end. He walked up to them slowly, stomping his heavy feet on the pavement. He was almost impossible to see because of the dark passageway and his dark clothes. When a car drove by flashing it's bright headlights behind him, René and the others saw that Fuentes wore a black shirt and navy blue bell-bottom pants pressed tightly against his muscular figure. He reminded René of a statue carved of black ivory he had once seen in a *botánica* window.

"Boys, remember what I told you: there's a big treasure in there," Fuentes said, "just waiting for us. Remember to hand it to me. I'll get plenty of money for you. Good green cash you deserve. I promise. I'll be with you all the way. You go in first, I'll follow later. I'll look out from that car in front of the garden. Climb the fence, cross that scuzzy old man's garden, brake the temple side door and go inside. I'll join you later, just wanna make sure no cops 'round. Go, go!"

His voice had a force and conviction that drew the gang's total attention, as if he'd always been their leader. Silvera, the roughest of the lot, sat motionless and listened intensely while rubbing his right thumb up and down the handle of his closed jackknife in his pants pocket. René looked at the black tunnel floor and jerked his head left and right towards each end. He felt uneasy and stupid robbing a place so close to home; 113 was just a few yards away from Mount Pisgah. It would be impossible to hide his tracks.

"Up, up!" Fuentes ordered. They rose quickly and followed him to the east end of the underpass, which faced the green-vined, wire-mesh fence of the temple garden.

Fuentes stayed where he was, watching the boys march out. He saw them look around before climbing over the fence one at a time with feline silence and swiftness. They disappeared into the thick shrubbery, breaking branches and stepping over the flowers, plants and vines and the tiny brook.

Gone from René's mind were the many times he had helped Silas Turnvil rake the black and brown soil, bury seeds, trim the hedges, or just sit back and watch the old man work and talk about the many books he had read and hoped that someday René would read, too. "Austen, Cervantes, Crane, Hesse, London, Melville, Twain, Zola, the guys you should know, René." Once in a while Silas felt so relaxed with his young listener that he spoke freely about his lifelong hopes and dreams, dreams which had never materialized. Don Quixote was a hero among fools," Silas always said. "Even on his death bed he saw visions impossible for others to see." René asked who this Don was. Silas laughed and scratched his beard, then told him the tale of the old Hidalgo.

Those thoughts were vanishing from René's mind, replaced by a fearless chill in him that drove him onward, like someone caught in rapids, hoping that somehow he would be led to the safety of dry land, somewhere down stream. If not, he would either be pulled to the bottom of the stream or get his head smashed against a boulder in the middle of his journey.

René led the gang into the garden because he was the only one familiar with it. He could avoid running into empty tin cans, glass bottles and the tiny warning bells which Turnvil had strung in certain spots. Many of his flowers had been stolen when they reached full bloom. And many were the times when, upon hearing the bells ring, he had run out with a crowbar and chased away the thieves. When the boys reached the temple side door, they pried it open with a spade they had found leaning against the back wall of the marble shop. They held their breaths when the swinging door produced a low rusty squeak. It sounded like a demonic squeal coming from the dark shadows of the temple's interior. They entered quickly and closed the door behind them as they felt a strange heat slap their perspiring faces.

Temple Mount Pisgah was constructed in 1911. It was a narrow building, compared to other city temples, with a broad wooden front doorway that swung out when opened. Once a popular house of worship, its 150-seat pews were often filled to capacity. After the Second World War, East Harlem changed its face and voice, but small pockets of its diverse past still remained by 1961. 116th Street was still Italian, 96th Street still Irish and German, 125th Street was and remained Negro. From the East End to the West End, some old synagogues still stood, mere echoes of a once Jewish Harlem. At Mount Pisgah, just a bare handful of aged worshipers still observed the Sabbath and high holy days. Two rows of mahogany pews lined the assembly, which was lit by several rows of metal bells with bare light bulbs screwed into their domes. A simple altar stood in front of a mahogany-paneled wall with Hebrew words carved into it's shiny surface. The urn of the Eternal Light before the Ark gave off a slight flicker. Groping in the dark, one of the boys found a light and pulled its beady chain. It lighted up a corner near the altar. They remained there, crouched beneath the small glow, as they had done in the underpass moments earlier while waiting for Fuentes.

Peering around to every corner, wall and nook, René tried to imagine what his eyes could not see. He found it difficult to believe that those voices—often sweet and full of feeling—he often heard singing and praying in that strange language actually came from this dark, hollow place, so full of shadows now and the sound of the gang's footsteps and heavy breathing. He jumped when Silvera nudged him in the ribs with his bony elbow.

"Where da fuck is Fuentes?" Silvera asked.

"I donno, but he better come quick. I don't dig dis place."

"I don't see no fucken gold," Dutch said. "I can't see a goddamn damn thing ... "

"Fellows," Fuentes said joining them. He squatted between

them. "See that tiny house—the ark—there in the middle of the altar? Break it open and take what's inside. René, pull those silver candle sticks from that wall. You guys, see what's in that big box near that Roman column. I'll look around for the strong box; I'm sure it's loaded."

Feeling his way along the edge of the pew Fuentes disappeared into the dark. Two boys pried open the ark and found a large double scroll inscribed in Hebrew. They threw it on the floor and poked their hands inside the ark again, tearing its cloth-lined interior, but found nothing. When René pulled down the candleholders, they slipped from his hands and broke in halves. They were old and the soft metal they were made of could not take the impact of the fall. He also found a blackened silver chalice on a tiny shelf, near the candleholders.

It reminded René of that day long, long ago when he had picked up the silver chalice dropped by a boy no different than he and how he had marveled at its rich glimmer. Then he remembered the harsh slap his mother had given him, the chalice flying out the window, the broken statue of the Virgin, María Cristina, Luz Castro's breasts, this dark temple, this tarnished cup, as empty as the feeling he felt deep within him.

Fuentes found a metal box on a wall near the front entrance and broke it open with a large screwdriver he had tucked under his belt. The box fell on the floor with a loud crack, spilling a number of coins on the floor, which scattered in all directions, near his feet, beneath the benches. Some hit Fuentes on the face as they slipped from his hands. There was no gold, no silver, no books bound in silver decorated with rubies, nor truckloads of coins and jewels. No bonds of any kind, no strong box with stacks of hundred dollar bills. In its place there lay papers they could not read, vestments they could not wear. Here lay the real bounty scattered on the old wooden floor: a fistful of miserable coins. Shocked and angry, the boys ran up to Fuentes and cursed him, as if he were a madman who had led them nowhere.

"Fuentes, you fuck! Dare ain't no gold here!" Silvera yelled.

"There's gotta be! I know it. I feel it. You know it. Keep looking. They say them Jews is rich! They say them Jews is smart! They hate me an' you! You boys say that all the time.

Tear the walls, search the basement, break the books in half, rip every piece of cloth you find until you find what you're looking for!" Fuentes yelled rapidly, raising his voice, clenching his fists and swinging his arms around. He walked in circles from one end of the altar to the other as he yelled, eyes aflamed, voice growing louder and louder until it turned into wolf-like howl. And his heavy eyebrows furrowed and seemed as if they wanted to squeeze his eyeballs from their sockets. Then Fuentes and his young followers heard a door squeal open and shut with a slam from a dark corner near the altar. René recognized the face and form of Silas Turnvil standing in the semi-darkness, brandishing a metal object in his right hand.

"Get out of here or I will break every one of your heads! If I have to kill each one of you, I will. By the living God that protects this holy temple, I'll kill you thieves and throw you into the gutter where you belong!" Turnvil breathed deeply and cursed at the dark figures before him. The gang stood between the first row of benches and the ark.

"Old man," Fuentes said stepping forth, "put that pipe down or I'll shove it down your ugly gullet. We come here for the treasure that you and your friends hide from the people of East Harlem. Give it to me and tomorrow morning you'll wake up alive. If not, take your last breath. We'll not leave empty-handed."

Silas Turnvil laughed aloud. "You make me laugh, *señor*. Tell me, do you talk to these boys the same way, you phoney? Get out!"

"You lousy old bum, where is the treasure that you hide from my boys?"

"In your hands, spare change. Buy whatever you can with it, there is no more," Turnvil said in a careworn voice. "Get out or I'll knock your heads off!" he yelled as he raised the metal pipe over his head and stepped forward.

Cindro Silvera stood behind the others, near the entrance, while Fuentes and Turnvil threatened each other. Lowering himself to a crouching position Silvera stepped back a few feet, then got on his belly and crawled around the benches, past the doors of the front entrance, down the center aisle until he was just a few feet in back of the old man. He then sprang up and landed on Turnvil's back, wrapping his legs around his waist. Silvera grabbed the old man by the front of his frock and pushed his face forward, while he punched the right side of Turnvil's face and head with his free hand and pounded his back with his fist, creating heavy thuds that nearly left the aging man breathless. With one backward swing of the club, Turnvil managed to hit Silvera on his left shoulder and knock him to the floor. Turnvil dropped to his knees, clenching his throat, and tried to straighten his back. Then he was knocked down by Fuentes, who dove at him and knocked him flat on his back. René and the others stared, unable to move as they tried to distinguish one man from the other. It was dark and both men struggled for their life, punching, kicking, cursing. Fuentes was strong, determined to kill Turnvil for a fistful of dollars. He had led the boys too far to let Turnvil chase them away empty-handed. Nut, slimy old man, miser, Jew ragman, I hate your blue eyes, cold stare, pale flesh, stale smell.

The shamas fought back with almost equal ferocity, punching, kicking, cursing Fuentes between clenched teeth. Bastard, scum, thief, maggot, I'll kill you, you rapist, Iago, Hitler.

While the men struggled, the gang ran to the side door, yanked it open, ran out to the garden rattling cans and bells and climbed the fence like frightened monkeys, then scattered in different directions. René turned his head to his left when he heard a groan that was almost as loud as those produced by the fighting men in front of him. He saw Silvera crawling on his knees, bleeding, crying, cursing until he reached the side entrance, got up and ran out. René stood still, not knowing what to do in that dark place which reminded him of those torturous moments he'd spent locked in his closet atoning for his sins.

Fuentes opened a cut in Turnvil's left cheek with a sharp jab which knocked him down. The sailor then sprang up and landed on Turnvil's upturned belly and held the lead pipe over the old man's head. Kneeling, René stared at the two men without moving. The wooden floor felt as if it was about to collapse beneath his feet. He thought about the endless summer: in Fuentes' grip, pushing drugs, making money that disappeared and left him penniless within a few hours, commanded like a slave, putting junkies in the gutter, handing them over to *Señor* Fuentes and to a worst hell than East Harlem. Eldorado, the empty dream, lost in a flash. Luz, Luz, baby, *mamá*, save me.

René was surprised to see Turnvil fight back so fiercely. For an old man, he seemed as strong as a bull who'd been kicked by horses, prodded by picadors, cut by matadors, bleeding, panting, facing the cold steel that would send him into oblivion. Turnvil sweated, cursed, almost seemed to be enjoying the fight, kicking, punching, sometimes laughing as he grinned like someone brought back to life after a long sleep.

But Fuentes overpowered Turnvil and jumped on his chest as the old man lay catching his breath, poking around the floor for the lead pipe. One good swing was all Fuentes needed to end Turnvil's life. The old man coughed and gave a howl like a trapped animal fighting for its life. The sailor found the metal pipe first and raised it high in the air, aiming it at the crazy old man's massive head.

René rose to his feet, still staring at the men and the shadows they cast on the walls of Mount Pisgah. He wanted to run away, but his legs wouldn't move, he felt paralyzed. The men were in the middle of the altar, in front of the open ark, the star of David above them on the stained glass windows, the holy scrolls with their commandments, psalms, epics laying near by. René saw Fuentes raise the pipe to strike Turnvil. In an instant—one eternal moment racked with torment, anger, confusion, courage, panic and love and hate for the old man and the sailor—René hurled the silver chalice at Fuentes. It struck him on his left temple, cut open a deep gash and knocked him down, off Turnvil's heaving chest.

"René!" Fuentes yelled as he fell beneath the altar.

"René!" Turnvil cried out.

The young man ran out of Temple Mount Pisgah, leaving the two men lying, bleeding and still cursing each other. Fuentes hid in the great shadows with his palms on his forehead. Silas Turnvil stared, silently panting, at a small light-bulb that hung swinging in its silent corner.

FOURTEEN

For what seemed the hundredth time that summer, René found himself trapped in a nightmare. He had run up the steps of 113 like a fleeing convict with a dozen hounds right behind him. He was about to open his door, when he suddenly remembered that his mother had taken his keys away. He ran out to the entrance of the silent building. Leaning over from the top step and holding on to the doorway's edge, he tried to pull the window open but found it also locked. He was not only being pursued, now he was also homeless. Every human shadow that passed behind him came to life, inching its way towards him. He tried once again to pull the window up, but it wouldn't budge. He ran down the steps, sprinted along the bare left wall of the building and entered through the kitchen window after a short climb. René moved with the feline swiftness and silence of a skilled burglar. Amanda slept soundly. He stepped inside the dark room and slipped into his narrow cot, fearing that his moves might betray him. He lay still, fully dressed, breathless, staring out the front window at the lights that came in from outside. Every inch of his body pulsed with a burning sensation. He opened the bottom half of the window. A mild breeze did little to cool his heated flesh. Within minutes he was fast asleep.

He twisted and turned, unable to find a cool spot where he could free himself from the dark figures that chased him. Every place he rested his head brought new visions that sprung at him with steel-trap strength. In a half awake state, he saw brief images which flashed before his eyes, smiling, laughing, yelling, crying, whispering at him. Sometimes hollow voices, like those in a carnival madhouse, jeered and mocked René in an endless din. "René, René. You're good, you're bad, you're ugly, you're beautiful. You have sinned! Out of the House of God! You are forgiven, my son.

145

Come to me. Touch me, touch me. Love me, love me. Kiss me and fuck me, my sweet little man. Sing to me, René. Go away! I will cut you and scatter your miserable skinny body into the black waters of the East River, never to be found. You are nothing, René—a worm, a flower, a petal, a drop of water, a piece of a mountain." Echoing, echoing voices in a tunnel without end. Sounds of water falling drowned the voices and shadows. He looked down at his hands and discovered that they had turned to mighty lion paws. He lashed out in all directions and yelled with a loud roar. René twisted, tossed, kicked and scratched at Fuentes until he realized that he was not dreaming.

Fuentes was hanging from the window sill with one hand and with his other had grabbed René by the throat as he lay sleeping. The grip was tight. René felt his breath leaving his body. He gasped and fought, but it was useless. He cursed and kicked at Fuentes, trying desperately to punch the sailor's bloody face. René was pulled from the bed's edge and landed on the window ledge, his stomach pressed against it's old wooden frame, which almost cut into his thin belly. René looked at Fuentes through burning, watery eyes. Fuentes seemed tired, panting, but raging and determined to kill. Fuentes pulled himself further into the room, bent his elbow and tightened his grip on René's windpipe, inching himself closer to his gasping victim. When Fuentes came closer, René lashed out and punched him across the jaw, like the young boxer had done to the champion beneath the blaze of the Cuban sun, long ago. But it was useless; the sailor's face was brick hard. No use struggling. Fuentes became a blur, the street lights in back of him merged into a red and green haze that drew him nearer and nearer. All sounds stopped. His head felt as hot as an iron just placed into a smith's anvil. Breathless, his punches getting weaker by the moment, he began to fall to his knees when he suddenly heard a scream, a loud thud, then a hand which pulled him back into the room.

Amanda swung a heavy wooden club at Fuentes, striking him several times before he loosened his grip. She hit him across the face and the side of his head. Fuentes released him and fell down, landing near the basement door.

"René!" Amanda yelled, dragging her son back inside. She ran across the room and turned on the lights. Then she got him a glass of water. He drank fast, in heavy gulps. Water never tasted so sweet.

"Who was that? What the hell happened?"

"Fuentes! He tried to kill me!"

"Fuentes?" she screamed.

"Yeah, dat rotten fuck. See, see, he's no fucken good! Tried to kill me."

Amanda slumped down beside René as he lay whiping his face with his bed sheet. A cut above his right eyebrow forced him to close his burning eyes. When he opened his eyes a few moments later, he saw his mother on her knees in the middle of the room, in front of the fireplace, rocking back and forth whispering loudly, "Fernando, Fernando! Why? Why? Who are you? What is love? What is love, dear God?" She looked tired, confused, hurt, hair bunched into a tight knot. She was dressed in a long white nightgown that reached her ankles and she still wielded the wooden club that she'd used on the man she thought she loved.

"I only wanted to get you nice things an' to get you an' me da hell out of dis fucken place. Fuentes is a liar, a pusher. Dare ain't no gold in da temple. No treasure. I'm tired. I don't care 'bout nothing no more," René said.

"Nothing?" Amanda asked with a painful stare.

René suddenly realized that his mother was deeply hurt. Too hurt to speak. He forgot about the struggle in the temple and his own pains. He felt numb all over, too weary to think or say anything that made sense. He clenched he fists, wanting to run after Fuentes, hurl a stone at him, bash his head open with an ax. No man had ever hurt his mother so much. No one had ever abused and tormented him the way Fuentes had. Never again would he let anyone push him around, terrify him, steal his mother's affection, command him like a slave, finally try to take his very life away and snuff out Mister Silas Turnvil, too. René was no longer afraid. Yet, he placed his head beneath his mother's chin when he sat quietly next to her on the floor, staring at the painted flowers on the tiled floor. He told her about Fuentes and what had happened between them. The burglary, the threat, the deal, the drug runs, the temple and now this.

She remained in a stupor, staring at the floral pattern beneath them as if it were a real garden. She stroked her son's head and told him to go to sleep. Before doing so, he poked his head out the window. Fuentes was gone. Amanda turned out the light and lay down, wishing she could turn off her thoughts just as easily: one flip, then blackness.

Unable to fall asleep, René lay still, staring at the dark ceiling. He got up several times to make sure the window was secure and the door locked with its metal chain and police lock. He tossed and turned quietly and fluffed his moist pillow, turning it over several times as he looked for a dry spot. He did not want to awaken his mother, though it seemed to him that she was tossing as much in her little corner near the kitchenette. She occasionally uttered a deep sigh and, in a faint whisper, *"Ay, Señor, ¿por qué?"* This went on for several hours until René, overcome with fatigue, was about to slip into a deep slumber when he was shaken awake again. Amanda screamed out, "René!" at the top of her voice and ran towards him.

In back of her, from the kitchen, a large red flash lit the kitchen as a blazing fire quickly engulf the area in front of the kitchen window, then spread within seconds to the rest of the kitchenette. Before René could move, Amanda grabbed him by an arm and pulled him off the bed, almost dragging him a few feet across the door. René scrambled to his feet and followed her out to the corridor, where they joined a stream of panicking half-naked tenants who were also trying to escape to safety.

Although it was nearly three o'clock in the morning, 103rd Street was teaming with curious people awakened by screams and bright light. Most of them lived across the street, others lived in the two furnished-room buildings between 113 and Mount Pisgah. The onlookers formed small groups and gasped as they watched the flames rapidly wave their way up the walls of the old house. Others looked out their windows in horror, crying, praying, crossing themselves. Within minutes, sirens filled the air as several fire engines made the quick two block dash from the firehouse on 104th Street near Third Avenue. They tore around the corner of Lexington and stopped dead in front of 113.

René and his mother were standing in the middle of the street when the speeding fire engines made them step back onto the opposite curb. A large group of firemen quickly jumped off the truck before it stopped, pulled a mammoth hose from it's van, connected it to the hydrant on the corner of Park and ran to the burning tenement.

"He has destroyed the house of the wicked in everlasting flames!" María Cristina Cruz yelled as she knelt on the sandy ground of the empty lot between the naked left side of 113 and the abandoned campaign stage. María Cristina stared at the building with a crazed look on her old face. With her hair disheveled, she seemed like a veritable corpse with opened eyes. Against her heaving bosom she held Jorge's picture and a Bible with a black beaded rosary hanging between it's back cover and the text. She rose and walked to the front of the building.

Amanda watched her for several minutes, then rushed up to her. María Cristina was lost in her madness and did not hear Amanda ask her if she was all right. She clasped her hands tighter and with trembling lips, continued yelling as she stared at the large flames that came from Amanda's open window.

"You serpents, you brood of vipers, how are you to escape being sentenced to hell?" The old woman raved at the people along the sidewalk and those looking out their windows.

"María!" Amanda yelled, but the mad woman could not hear, nor see anything but the voices inside her.

"If any one comes to me and does not hate his own father and mother and wife and children and brothers and sisters, yes, and even his own life, he cannot be my disciple!"

"María!" Amanda yelled again, with a savage look on her face. "What have you done? What happened?"

"I don't know ... " María Cristina replied, coming to her senses.

"Your candles, your altar near the window, did it start the fire?"

"Maybe," María Cristina sobbed. She now held the rosary, gripping it's beads and crucifix between trembling hands. "It doesn't matter anymore. I'm lost, you're lost, little René is gone, although he stands nearby, Luz Castro is burning. So is the *Judío* ... "

"What have you done, you crazy old woman! My home is gone, my son is a man, and the man I loved is a phantom that never was ... " Amanda's voice trailed down to a mere whisper. She felt so weak and weary that her knees began to buckle and was about to slump down on the sidewalk, when René ran up to her and grabbed her by the arm and waist. He sat her on a middle step of 112 and sat himself across a landing in back of her, resting her back against an outer leg, holding her trembling shoulders with his hands.

"Dat crazy ole lady burned our home down," René said. "She ought to be there, inside!"

"Father, Father, forgive us. Protect us. Love us. I don't want to die! Sanctified is your name and your being. Forgive us, give us another chance so we can build the world you desire so much ... " María Cristina now chanted and uttered vows of contrition, as if awakening from a nightmare, although the flames continued to burn bright before her living eyes. Words, words lost in the night as fast as yesterday's dreams.

René stared at the red, yellow and blue flames that came from his window. The entire block was as bright as a new dawn as the fire increased with each passing minute. A huge cloud of grey and black smoke and steam rose up into the lighted sky and turned with a gust of wind back onto the tenement, nearly obscuring it, Mount Pisgah, the railroad and East 103rd Street. Never again would René slip in and out of that very window. The window was broken, the long room was entombed in a bright light as fierce and unapproachable as a furnace. The wooden door of the front entrance of the house was wide open. From where he sat, René could still see the long corridor of the first floor. The stairway was engulfed in flames. The firemen's hoses were aimed at the top floor and roof, where it rained down in a heavy torrent.

As René stared at the fire, he suddenly saw the figure of a man, covered with a thick, wet blanket, making his way towards the entrance. The wall of flames in back of him hid his blackened face, but René was still able to recognize the tall, bearded and stoop-shouldered figure of Silas Turnvil. René jumped up and ran across the street, skipped up the stone steps and dove into the house. Amanda looked up and screamed, then ran after him, but a fireman grabbed her by the waist and stopped her at the foot of the stairs.

Inside, René quickly grabbed Turnvil as he staggered forward. The old man was coughing and waving his arms and fists at the fire, trying to fight his way out of the inferno. Turnvil was so overcome by the fumes and flames that he let René pull him a few steps forward, then down the front steps of 113. The firemen now attacked the house with several more jetting hoses, crowbars and hooks. When René reached the street, he leaned Turnvil against a parked car and sprinkled water from a moving stream along the curb onto the old man's face.

Amanda ran up to them.

"René! You stupid little fool! You could've gotten killed."

"I'm all right, Mom."

"An' you, old man, you almos' got my son killed."

Turnvil stared at her with glazed eyes. His mind miles away. She turned away, then walked up to María Cristina, who sat alone with her back pressed against the black iron railing along the front of 112. Amanda looked down at her and felt pity for her. Still sobbing and whispering to herself, María Cristina reminded Amanda of her grandmother: penitent, sober, caring, wild, yet strange and out of place, like a spirit from the past that refuses to leave this world. But Amanda was too angry and too overwrought to forgive this mad woman. Her grandmother was a true saint, compared to this miserable wreck. Amanda cursed María Cristina again in a loud voice.

"See what you've done, stupid fool!"

"Leef da ole lady alone!" someone from an upper floor of 112 cried at Amanda.

"No, I did nothing," María Cristina said in a daze. "I only lit a few candles and prayed that Cristo save me when he comes to El Barrio. He blew my curtains near a candle, which caught fire ... but he saved me by keeping me awake all night. When I saw the flames reach the ceiling, I ran out. I don't want to die! But ... "

"*¡Estúpida!* You were saved because you ran out on time, not because He loves you or any damn priest, nun, evangelist, Jew, Moslem, Buddhist—whatever!—more than me and René."

"No, Amanda. I was saved because I serve Him—unlike them!" She stood up and pointed a trembling finger at a couple which suddenly emerged from Luz Castro's window. The couple appeared to be naked, but they were not. The man's groin was covered by a pair of very tight briefs. The woman only wore a white pantie; she covered her bare chest with her folded arms. They both yelled for help as they clung to one another on the edge of the fire escape.

Amanda looked up and recognized Fernando and Luz. For a few brief moments, Amanda stared up frightfully as she saw her two friends desperately trying to flee to safety. She felt an urge to scream out and run to them, but she stopped when she realized they were near naked, glimmering from the light of the flames and heat. Amanda's passion turned into anger. It was obvious to Amanda that these two were more than just friends. Betrayed by both of them, Amanda wished that the two would burn in the hell that the pious María Cristina had created with her devotions and carelessness. A ladder was propped up against the building and a fireman ascended towards them. He guided Luz down and told Fernando to follow. They descended the shaky ladder quickly and jumped down onto the street when they reached the bottom of the steps. A woman in the crowd then ran across the street with two bed sheets and covered them.

Fernando and Luz rested their aching and partly scorched bodies against the face of the synagogue, clenching the thin sheets that draped them like togas. Amanda walked up to them, placed her hands on the tops of both sheets and, with a strong pull, yanked them down to the ground. She stepped back a few feet and stared at the pair, then burst out in a fit of mad laughter. A loud chorus of laughter erupted behind Amanda. Too angry to speak, Amanda stared at the pair in disbelief. Fernando and Luz said nothing. René joined his mother and tried to pull her back across the street. He felt an urge to laugh at the mad scene, just like his mother, but remained deadpan. There was Fuentes, naked as a monkey and powerless to hurt anyone. No drugs, threats, knives, too drunk to care.

"The sea will always be there waiting for me, she is the only good woman," Fuentes said to himself in a low whisper. And Luz Castro, with her long black hair licked by the swift flames, standing between the temple and the garden, naked, lost, deeply wounded by sudden shock, with nowhere to turn but far, far away from the heart of East Harlem.

That bastard Fuentes has even taken her away from me, René lamented. Bitch, bitch! Yet, she still looked beautiful to René. Luz was totally illuminated by the red and white light coming from 113, like a naked marble Venus before a wandering lover in the dead of night. René turned his face towards his vanishing home and saw a thin rainbow, just barely visible in the spray which rained down on the house. Fernando and Luz picked up the sheets and covered themselves. Fernando and Luz, still drape in sheets, walked over to Park Avenue and headed uptown to his place.

Silas was laid on a stretcher and was about to be placed in a municipal ambulance nearby, when he told the orderlies to stop. He coughed several times, smiled at René and squeezed his hands.

"René, I don't know if I'll return. Take care of the garden, will you? Help it grow. There is a white rose which sprung up between the trees in the garden. I've never seen one like it. I didn't plant it. Neither did you nor Rabbi Simon. It's still alive and growing despite the summer heat. Still yearning for rain, sunlight, wind. I have the feeling it will always be there, almost touching that ailanthus tree near the fence corner." He coughed hard.

"Take it easy, old man. Be still. I'm okay now, because I ain't afraid of nothin' or nobody. I ain't lettin' no one push me or mom around. I'd keep your books and papers for you, but they're all gone."

"No, they're not gone."

"Dey were burnt."

"They will never die; it's all we have. If they die, so will we."

"Sorry I tried to hurt you."

"You didn't hurt me. You saved my life."

"No. I mean back dare in da temple."

"Forget it, sonny. We all make mistakes. Remember what I said ... " When Turnvil coughed again, an ambulance orderly placed an oxygen mask over his nose and mouth. The orderly and a nurse then placed him inside the van and sped away with its lights flashing and its siren screaming towards Second Avenue.

As the flames died down, the trains continued to speed by East Harlem. The heavy waterfall from the firemen's hoses streamed down the building, leaving in its path a stream of cinder and ash, fire and brimstone—volcanic splendor in the middle of a great city. The water finally dowsed the inferno that had devoured 113. After borrowing some clothes and shoes from friends in 112, René and Amanda walked away towards Lexington, where a subway train

took them to a relative's home in the south Bronx. Amanda thought
about how sudden and strong the rain in Puerto Rico is, and how
swiftly it subsides. René remembered the story of the hidden
waterfall in his grandparents' old home; he wondered if there was
ever such a place. No, couldn't be. It no longer mattered.

Within two weeks, Amanda and René were once again living
in another furnished room in East Harlem. She'd found a steady
job as a waitress in a diner on 125th Street and Second Avenue,
borrowed a few dollars and rented a large room similar to the one
on East 103rd Street. This new one was situated on the north end
of the barrio. It was a big room with a fine view of a line of old
brownstones with small trees planted in front of each house. One
day, Amanda noticed that some grape crates were piled neatly in
front of the building across the street beneath a young sidewalk
tree. A handful of the fermented grapes had fallen on the solid
ground. Amanda watched as a blue jay with a white crest swooped
from a tree branch, picked up a grape with its beak and flew away.
Amanda let go of the curtain and turned away.

A month or so later, René took a walk one bright spring day and
found himself by chance near his old block. He turned the corner
and continued his stroll until he reached 113. Since the fire, René
had visited the old block twice to work in the garden. Rabbi Abe
Simon told him that Turnvil had vanished; there was no sign of
him anywhere. The temple was nearly deserted, its members now
numbered less than a dozen. It would only be a matter of time
before Mount Pisgah's doors would close indefinitely. The garden
needed no one. God, Rabbi Simon told him, would give it life.

As René walked away, he stopped in front of 113 and discovered
that a bulldozer had raised it to the ground, reducing it to a large
mound that reached the same level as where the first floor had been.
He ascended the knoll and looked around. Parts of the yellow
painted wall of his room still remained, three or four feet above
the rubble, surrounded by dirt and fallen brick. Although most of
the tenants had carted away what wasn't destroyed by the fire, there
remained pieces of broken furniture, sinks, bathtubs, rusty pipes,
broken pictures, toys, clothes and food. Several of Silas Turnvil's
precious volumes lay strewn about the rubble; some spilled out to
the empty lot, naked, scorched, as weathered and beautiful as the

Dead Sea Scrolls. He dusted off a few and placed them under his left arm.

René stepped on a sharp metal object which almost tore the thin sole of his sneakers. He jumped back and looked down. He squatted and with his fingers raked the sand and stones away from the object. It was a small tin box, similar to one he had once seen on Turnvil's workbench. He picked it up and blew off the dry earth on it's lid. Not knowing what to make of it, René quickly opened it, hoping he would find something of value. He found a parcel of very old letters wrapped in a leather bag, yellowed by time and partially burnt by the heat of the fire. They reminded him of some of the prayer scrolls he had seen in the temple. He held the fragments close to his face and tried to read the faded words.

> Dear Silas,
> Several weeks have passed since I last saw you and I cannot bear the separation. Here in the green countryside, I can at last breath fresh air that hopefully will clear my lungs of my illness and that awful city air. I take long walks every day where Emily Dickenson once strolled, and where you can still sit and live without worrying that some desperate soul will take away your life. I had to get away from East Harlem and wish you would do the same. What is it about that place that holds you so much? Is it more important than me? How can anyone like that noise they call music, that odd manner of dress, those strange smells and that infernal chatter which is a butchering of beautiful Spanish? Why, Silas, why? What is it about East Harlem, with its teaming strangers and daily horror, that attracts you so much? I don't know. Perhaps I never will. I insist we sell the bookshop and move. Here, preferably. No one around there reads anymore. That old spinster, Dickenson, once wrote that love, love of all things, is the only real reason we exist. I wish I could feel that way. Yet, it was love that drew me to you and love that brought me here to these

hills. And it is love that will always draw me to
you. Silas, remember that I am always with you.
Though you cannot see me, our souls are one.
Wish you were here.

Love, Elly

René put the letters back in the bag, dropped the box and returned to the garden where he buried the letters beneath the ailanthus tree. Then he turned and walked down the street, where he
disappeared into a crowd of people, still thinking about the old
man and how much he loved that little spot on the corner of Park
Avenue.

113 was torn down along with the two buildings adjacent to
Temple Mount Pisgah. The temple stood silent for several more
years until it succumbed to the constant onslaughts of thieving van-
dals, who robbed it of its meager holdings again and again. The
army in sneakers, jeans and garrison belts tore away its marble
slabs and several brass light domes. They stole Menorahs and carried away the spoils of the Temple, like Roman soldiers marching
through the Arch of Titus. When there was nothing left of the hollow building, they burned it to the ground one cold black night in
the dead of winter, while the people of East 103rd Street slept. The
wire fence, now rusted by time, still corrals that spot that was once
a beautiful garden. It is overgrown with wild flowers and tall, rich
green plants, untouched by human hands. As René walked away
that day in the spring, he smiled when he saw children laughing,
running, crying and raising dust on the hallowed ground.